BRAIN GAMES™

Word Puzzles

Publications International, Ltd.

Puzzle Consultants: Adam Cohen, Julie K. Cohen, Shawn Kennedy, Amy Reynaldo

Puzzle Constructors: Michael Adams, Deb Amlen, Sam Bellotto Jr., George Bredehorn, Myles Callum, Clarity Media, Jeff Cockrell, Don Cook, Mark Danna, Harvey Estes, Josie Faulkner, Luke Haward, Helene Hovanec, Marilynn Huret, John McCarthy, Dan Meinking, Priscilla Meinking, David Millar, Dan Moore, Michael Moreci, Elsa Neal, Alan Olschwang, Fred Piscop, Stephen Ryder, Pete Sarjeant, Fraser Simpson, Terry Stickels, Wayne Robert Williams, John Wilmes

Illustrators: Helem An, Chris Gattorna, Elizabeth Gerber, Robin Humer, Shavan Spears, Jen Torche

Cover Puzzles: John McCarthy, Wayne Robert Williams

Cover Image: Shutterstock.com

ISBN-13: 978-1-4508-6439-8
ISBN-10: 1-4508-6439-2

Manufactured in U.S.A.

8 7 6 5 4 3 2 1

Work Out with Words!

It's important to keep our bodies and minds in good shape. You already know how to get physically fit: Get out there and exercise! To get mentally fit, however, you need to flex your mental muscles.

The best way to do that is both easy and fun: Brain research shows that working puzzles is a terrific way to retain—and gain—mental fitness. Puzzles require focused attention, mental flexibility, and problem-solving skills, all of which are important cognitive functions. So working puzzles is a mini brain workout. And the more you work out with puzzles, the more mental muscle you will develop.

Brain Games™: Word Puzzles is chock-full of mini workouts designed to help you build and hone your language skills. Inside you'll find an assortment of puzzles, including anagrams, word jigsaws, codewords, crosswords, cryptograms, and much, much more. If you get stuck, all puzzle answers can be found at the back of the book.

The puzzles are organized into 5 difficulty levels, from Very Easy to Expert. Start at the beginning, or jump in wherever you feel comfortable—you can customize your own mental workout! And since the book is easy to take along with you, you'll be able to enjoy a puzzle break no matter where you go.

1 | Wedgewords

Fit the words into the grid reading across and down. Each word is used once. Two letters have been given to get you started.

ASIA

EASE

EVIL

PEAL

PEEP

PRAY

RAVE

YELL

2 | Elevator Words

Like an elevator, words move up and down the "floors" of this puzzle. Starting with the first answer, the second part of each answer carries down to become the first part of the following answer. With the clues given, complete the puzzle.

1. Look _____   1. "Watch it!"

2. _____   2. Jesse James, for one

3. _____   3. Claim in court

4. _____   4. Traveler's need

5. _____ _____   5. Scientific analysis

6. _____ _____   6. High school period

7. _____way   7. Passage in a house

3 | Word Jigsaw

Fit the pieces into the frame to form common words reading across and down. There's no need to rotate the pieces; they'll fit as shown, with each piece used exactly once.

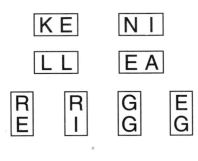

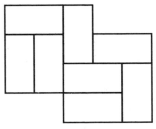

4 | Theme Park

This "ride" has a theme, but we can't tell you what it is. Place all the words in the boxes below—when you do, read the word created in the outlined boxes, from top to bottom, to reveal what the theme is.

LOAN

MORTGAGE

CHECKS

DEBIT

CREDIT

ATM

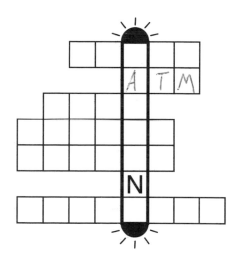

5 | Food Fun for Fans

A rebus follows its own type of alphabet: a mixture of letters, symbols, and pictures. Look carefully at the rebus below. You should be able to "read" the answer to the clue in the puzzle's title.

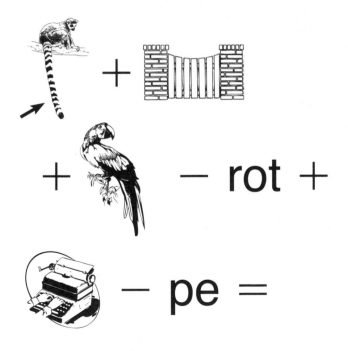

$+$

$+$ $-$ rot $+$

$-$ pe $=$

6 | Add-a-Word

Add one word to each of the 3-word sets to create new words or phrases. For example: In a set including "smith," "fore," and "game," the added word would be "word" (creating "wordsmith," "foreword," and "word game").

1. pad, tiger, pond: _____

2. tea, hips, prim: _____

3. saving, amazing, note: _____

4. Christmas, wood, hock: _____

5. stick, kill, ride: _____

6. liquid, clear, ball: _____

7 | What a Jewel

ACROSS

1. Faucet
4. Came in first
7. Animal's foot
10. Three in old Rome
11. Carnival city
12. "Birds _____ feather…"
13. Oz's capital, with "the"
16. Go bad
17. Greek war god
18. Hawaiian naval base
23. Flood barrier
24. Take five
25. Bullfight bravo
26. Something found in 13-, 18-, 34-, and 38-Across
27. Actress Gardner
30. Low in fat
32. Desert stopover
34. Arizona ballplayer or deadly snake
36. Sleeve fillers
37. Wedding oath
38. 1967 Rolling Stones hit
43. It may be inflated
44. Hobbit foe
45. Pilot's announcement, for short
46. Donkey
47. Hour past midnight
48. Use a Singer

DOWN

1. _____ the knot (get married)
2. Prepare to shoot
3. South Dakota's capital
4. Fury
5. Squeak solution application
6. Start to drift off
7. Fictional detective Hercule
8. Following
9. Methods
14. Part for an actor
15. They're often hailed
18. Mideast political grp.
19. Snaky fish
20. Madison or Fifth in NYC
21. "If there _____ objections…"
22. Famed Georgia band
26. Pinup's leg
27. Cool _____ cucumber
28. Singer Damone
29. Pop the question

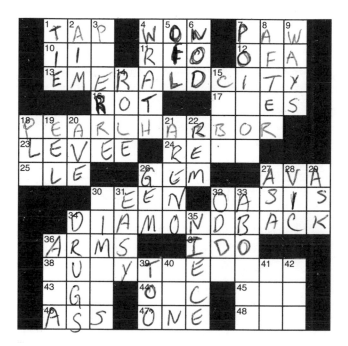

	T	A	P		W	O	N		P	A	W
I				R	F	O		O		F	A
E	M	E	R	A	L	D		C	I	T	Y
		R	O	T					E	S	
P	E	A	R	L	H	A	R	B	O	R	
L	E	V	E	E		R	E				
	L	E			G	U	M			A	V	A
			E	E	N		O	A	S	I	S
D	I	A	M	O	N	D	B	A	C	K	
A	R	M	S			I	D	O			
	U		Y	T	E				A		
G			O		C			5			
A	S	S		O	N	E					

30. Dances under a pole
31. Simple
32. 5:1, say, at a racetrack
33. Dwellings
34. Pharmaceuticals
35. Nephew's sister

36. Region
39. _____ close for comfort
40. Coffee dispenser
41. Had a bite
42. Swerve, as a sailboat

8| We, the Jury by Alpha Sleuth™

Move each of the letters below into the grid on the next page to form common words. You will use each letter once. The letters in the numbered cells of the grid correspond to the letters in the phrase below the grid. Completing the grid will help you complete the phrase and vice versa. When finished, the grid and phrase will be filled with valid words, and you will have used all the letters in the letter set.

Hint: The numbered cells in the grid are arranged alphabetically, so the letter in the cell marked 1 will appear in the alphabet before the letter in the cell marked 2, and so on.

A	B	C	D	E	F	G	H	I	J	K	L	M
N	O	P	Q	R	S	T	U	V	W	X	Y	Z

9 | Anagram Sentences

What 2 words, formed from different arrangements of the same 3 letters, can be used to complete the sentences below?

1. _____ that I have my _____ car, I can drive anywhere I like.

2. She caught _____ butterflies in her _____.

3. _____ taught you _____ to dance?

4. She kept sticks of _____ in a _____ on her desk.

10 | Diamond Cut

Follow the arrows to solve each clue and complete the grid.

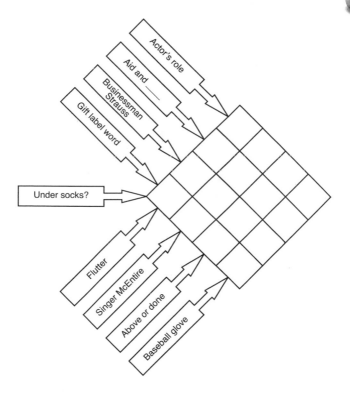

Actor's role

Aid and ___

Businessman Strauss

Gift label word

Under socks?

Flutter

Singer McEntire

Above or done

Baseball glove

11 | E Pyramid

To build this pyramid, we begin by placing an **E** at the very top. To find the answer to each consecutive clue and fill in the remaining layers, add a letter to the previous answer as you move downward.

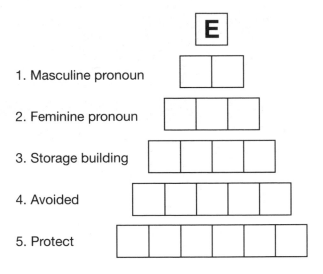

1. Masculine pronoun

2. Feminine pronoun

3. Storage building

4. Avoided

5. Protect

12 | Fitting Words

In this miniature crossword, the clues are listed
randomly and are numbered for convenience only.
It is up to you to figure out the placement of the
9 answers. To help you, we've inserted one letter in
the grid, and this is the only occurrence of that letter
in the completed puzzle.

1. Racetrack bet

2. Sunburn soother

3. Breathing

4. Satanic

5. Telephone greeting

6. _____, liquid, or gas

7. Try again

8. Laundry

9. Fish's breathing organ

13 | Divas

Every name listed is contained within the group of letters on the next page. Words can be found in a straight line horizontally, vertically, or diagonally. They may read either forward or backward.

ALICIA KEYS

ARETHA FRANKLIN

BEYONCÉ

BRITNEY SPEARS

CELINE DION

CHER

DIDO

DOLLY PARTON

ENYA

INDIA.ARIE

LADY GAGA

LEONA LEWIS

MADONNA

MARIAH CAREY

MARY J. BLIGE

MILEY CYRUS

NATALIE COLE

PINK

REBA

RIHANNA

SHAKIRA

SHERYL CROW

TAYLOR SWIFT

TINA TURNER

TONI BRAXTON

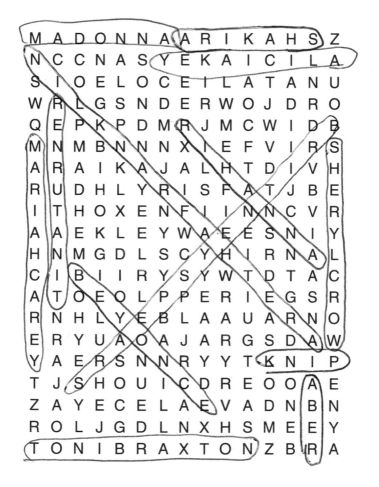

14 | Cryptogram

Cryptograms are messages in substitution code.
Break the code to read the humorous quote and
its source. For example, THE SMART CAT might
become FVO QWGDF JGF if **F** is substituted for **T**,
V for **H**, **O** for **E**, and so on.

"CVV UAIGDL TVCLDJO CJD

MBVBFZRCV. SUDL GFAQ DFZVBOU CFH

TJAXCFBSL."

—ZAJHBD UAQD

_____

_____

_____

_____

15 | Rhyme Time

Each clue leads to a 2-word answer that rhymes, such as BIG PIG or STABLE TABLE. The numbers in parentheses after the clue give the number of letters in each word. For example, "cookware taken from the oven (3, 3)" would be "hot pot."

1. Hoodlum insect (4, 3): _____ _____

2. Brag more than anyone else (5, 4):

   _____ _____

3. Speedy selection (5, 4): _____ _____

4. Tree's black coat (4, 4): _____ _____

5. Visually uninspiring room for experiments (4, 3):

   _____ _____

6. Tin or iron flower part (5, 5):

   _____ _____

7. Opulent financial institution (5, 4):

   _____ _____

8. Moist postage (4, 5): _____ _____

16 | The Highly Paid Actress from Down Under

What 2 words that are different arrangements of the same 5 letters can be used to complete the sentence below?

Considering how much critics panned the remake of "The Stepford _Wives_" Nicole Kidman probably _Made_ her decision to star in the movie as not one of her wiser career moves.

17 | Hobby Horse

Which of these is NOT an anagram for a pleasant hobby?

A. Try Poet

B. Rail Log

C. Goat Bin

D. Sigh Fin

18 | Grid Fill

To complete this puzzle, place the given letters and words into the shapes in this grid. Words and letters will run across, down, and wrap around each shape. When the grid is filled, each row will contain one of the following words: clear, dunce, earth, salty, shade, spoon.

1. R, Y

2. CS, SS

3. EON, HAD

4. DEAL, REAL, THAT

5. POUNCE

19 | J. Lo

ACROSS

1. Tack on
4. Up to the task
8. Lions, Tigers, or Bears
12. Tell a whopper
13. Dry as dust
14. Diva's delivery
15. 2003 J. Lo single
17. J. Lo's ex-husband, _____ Anthony
18. Trombone part
19. Sip from a flask
21. "The Simpsons" teacher Krabappel
24. British noblewomen
28. Square footage
31. "I'm _____ your tricks!"
33. "The Spirit" actress Mendes
34. "The _____" (2000 J. Lo movie)
35. Cake candle count
36. "_____ in Manhattan" (2002 J. Lo movie)
37. _____-o'-shanter
38. "Mask" actress
39. Model Macpherson
40. Big name in fine china
42. Hitchhiker's hope

44. Key near the space bar
46. Astrological ram
50. 1998 animated J. Lo movie
53. 1997 J. Lo movie
56. One of five in a limerick
57. Nursery rhyme trio
58. Aunts, uncles, etc.
59. Butter servings
60. They're splitsville
61. Take a gander at

DOWN

1. "Woe is me!"
2. Kind of pickle
3. Place to buy pickles
4. Oohed and _____
5. Victoria's Secret buy
6. Tyler of the "Lord of the Rings" movies
7. Noted garden
8. Florida city near St. Pete
9. The Gay Nineties, e.g.
10. Run on TV
11. Big _____ (burger)
16. Best possible
20. Altar vow
22. Old Testament shipbuilder

Across grid (handwritten answers):

- 1. ADD
- 4. ABLE
- 8. TEAM / M
- 12. LIE
- 13. ARID
- 14. ARIA
- 15. ALL
- 16. IHAVE
- 17. MARC
- 18. SLIDE
- 19. NIP
- 21. DNA
- 24. DAMES
- 28. (ELE...)
- 31. ONTO
- 33. EVA
- 34. EL
- 35. AGE
- 36. MAD
- 37. M
- 38. CHER
- 39. ELLE
- 40. O
- 41. LIFT
- 46. ACES
- 45.
- 50.
- 53.
- 56.
- 57.
- 58.
- 59.
- 60.
- 61.

Clues:

23. "_____ Eyes" (2001 J. Lo movie)
25. Rarity on flights, nowadays
26. The devil's doing
27. The Marquis de _____
28. Variety show segments
29. Gather, as rewards
30. Ticklish Muppet
32. Actress Hatcher
36. One "M" in MGM
38. Cartoon frame

41. Knocks senseless
43. Stands up to
45. Like a broken bronco
47. Autographs, informally
48. Actress Falco
49. All there, mentally
50. Swiss peak
51. Actress Long
52. Blaster's need, briefly
54. Give thumbs-down to
55. Up-one's-sleeve card

20 | Tangled Words

Think of this puzzle like a word search, only in reverse. Rather than finding the words in the grid, your job is to fill them in. Words begin only from the letters given in the shaded boxes, and they appear in a straight line horizontally, vertically, or diagonally. They may appear forward or backward. When complete, every word will have been used, and the grid will have no empty squares.

ARTICHOKE	COOKIE
ASPARAGUS	CORN
BEEF	CRUMB
BRIE	CURRY
BROTH	FISH
BURGER	FLUKE
BUTTER	HAM
CABBAGE	LEMON
CAKE	MACARONI
CARROTS	OKRA
CLAM	ONION

L									C	S
					C		S		A	
			O							
				H			P			
O			R	B				F		
							S	S		R
B			C				T			
B										C
				F					A	
	S						S			M
				C	B					

PASTRY

RAISIN

RICE

SCROD

SHAD

SIRLOIN

SPAM

SPROUTS

SYRUP

TREACLE

21 | Wedgewords

Fit the words into the grid reading across and down.
Each word is used once. Two letters have been
given to get you started.

AREA	ELSE
CAPE	MESS
COME	ORAL
EASE	PASS

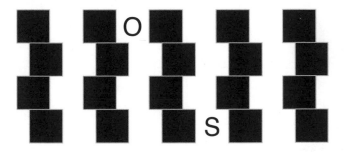

22 | Name Calling

Decipher the encoded word in the quip below using the numbers and letters on the phone pad. Remember that each number can stand for 3 or 4 possible letters.

As soon as you have graduated from the school of experience, someone adds a new 2–6–8–7–7–3.

23 | Fitting Words

In this miniature crossword, the clues are listed randomly and are numbered for convenience only. It is up to you to figure out the placement of the 9 answers. To help you, we've inserted one letter in the grid, and this is the only occurrence of that letter in the completed puzzle.

1. Part of a book

2. Opposite of verbose

3. Cashews and almonds

4. Give a paddling to

5. Slightly open, as with a door

6. "Shoo!"

7. ". . . with a banjo on my _____"

8. Louisiana cuisine

9. Glass marble

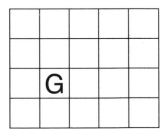

24 | Word Ladder

Use the clues to change just one letter on each line to go from the top word to the bottom word. Do not change the order of the letters. You must have a common English word at each step.

JOKE

_____ fuel made from coal

_____ holds ice cream

_____ offers support

_____ not crazed

SAME

25 | Between the Lines

Below are five 3-word sets, where the middle word is undefined. All 3 words in each set are arranged in alphabetical order. Unlocking the defined words makes it possible to discover the middle word. When complete, rearrange the middle words in the spaces at the bottom of the next page to reveal a quote from Titus Plautus.

Example: **putter:** to work at random; tinker
puzzle
pygmy: one of a race of dwarfs

1. ___ ___ ___ ___ ___ ___ ___ ___ ___:
retaining freshness year-round

___ ___ ___ ___ ___

___ v ___ ___ ___ ___ ___ ___: something
that furnishes proof

2. ___ ___ ___ ___ ___ c h: a second contest
between the same teams

___ ___ ___ ___ ___ y

___ ___ ___ ___ ___ ___ ___ ___: to think
of again

3. ___ ___ ___ ___: moderately fast gait of a horse

___ ___ o u ___ ___ ___

___ ___ ___ ___ g h: long narrow container for animals to drink or eat from

4. ___ ___ ___ ___ ___ ___ ___ ___: pitifully inferior or inadequate

___ ___ ___ ___ ___ ___ ___ ___

___ ___ t i e ___ ___: person receiving medical treatment

5. ___ ___ ___ ___ ___ ___: next to

___ ___ ___ ___

___ ___ ___ ___: second letter of the Greek alphabet

" _____ is the _____ _____ for

_____ _____."

26 | Flower Girls

The letters in CAMELLIA can be found in boxes 2, 6, 7, 8, 9, and 14 but not necessarily in that order. Similarly, the letters in all the other girl's names can be found in the boxes indicated. Your task is to insert all the letters of the alphabet into the boxes on the next page. If you do this correctly, the shaded cells will reveal another flower-inspired girl's name.

Hint: Compare VIOLA and VIOLET to get the value of **A**, then VIOLET and ROSE for the value of **T**.

CAMELLIA: 2, 6, 7, 8, 9, 14

DAISY: 6, 7, 10, 12, 18

HEATHER: 2, 3, 7, 13, 16

HOLLY: 12, 14, 16, 19

IRIS: 6, 10, 13

JASMINE: 2, 5, 6, 7, 9, 10, 17

LILY: 6, 12, 14

MAGNOLIA: 5, 6, 7, 9, 14, 15, 19

MARGUERITE: 2, 3, 4, 6, 7, 9, 13, 15

MARIGOLD: 6, 7, 9, 13, 14, 15, 18, 19

MYRTLE: 2, 3, 9, 12, 13, 14

POPPY: 1, 12, 19

ROSE: 2, 10, 13, 19

VIOLA: 6, 7, 11, 14, 19

VIOLET: 2, 3, 6, 11, 14, 19

1		14	
2		15	
3		16	
4		17	
5		18	
6		19	
7		20	B
8		21	F
9		22	K
10		23	Q
11		24	W
12		25	X
13		26	Z

27 | Add-a-Word

Add one word to each of the 3-word sets to create new words or phrases. For example: In a set including "smith," "fore," and "game," the added word would be "word" (creating "wordsmith," "foreword," and "word game").

1. box, mold, flat: _____

2. alcohol, wood, whole: _____

3. French, champagne, master: _____

4. safe, barrel, fire: _____

5. nut, sour, boy: _____

6. call, pay, bank: _____

28 | Split Decisions

Fill in each set of empty cells with letters that will create English words reading both across and down. Letters may repeat within a single set. We've completed one set to get you started.

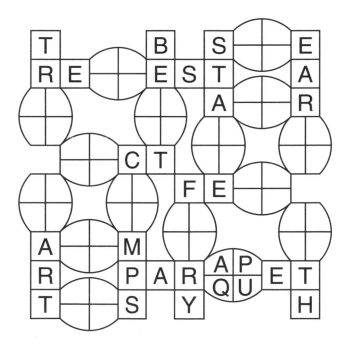

EASY

Answer each clue with a 6-letter word. Write the words in either a clockwise or counterclockwise direction around the numerals in the grid. We've placed some letters to get you started.

CLOCKWISE

1. Avoids capture
2. Grown-ups
3. Funeral songs
4. Lubricate
5. Soft and easy
6. Up and out of bed
7. Engineless plane
8. Most kind
12. Lying face upward
13. Light teasing
19. Open to all
20. Traveled from place to place
24. Process food
26. Dotty
28. Kitchen appliances
30. Lawn-care equipment
31. Lookout man
32. Relishes
33. AAA suggestions
34. Wind in a spiral course

COUNTERCLOCKWISE

9. Canal vessels
10. Instant
11. Quick look
14. Ill will
15. Outdoor meal
16. Commuter's destination
17. Boring routine
18. Boat basin
21. Domesticators
22. Wryly humorous
23. Increase 100 percent
25. Powerful speaker
27. Like a fuddy-duddy
29. Male singers
35. Supporting pieces
36. Turn around
37. Scenic route

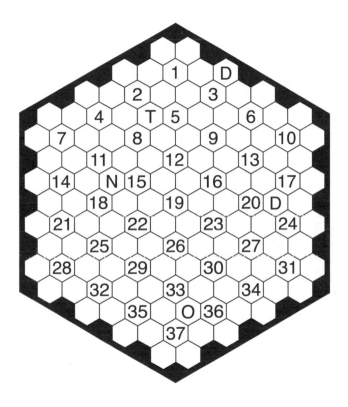

30 | Word Jigsaw

Fit the pieces into the frame to form common words reading across and down. There's no need to rotate the pieces; they'll fit as shown, with each piece used exactly once.

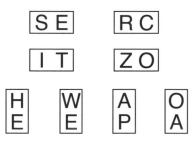

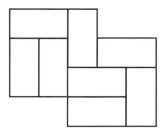

31 | Frame Games™

Can you "read" the phrase below?

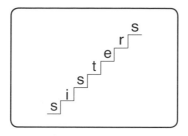

32 | Frame Games™

Can you "read" the phrase below?

33 | Sports Legends

Go for the gold, and find every sports legend listed within the group of letters on the next page. Words can be found in a straight line horizontally, vertically, or diagonally. They may read either forward or backward.

AMY ALCOTT	MIA HAMM
BONNIE BLAIR	MICHELLE KWAN
CHRIS EVERT	NANCY LOPEZ
(KIM) CLIJSTERS	(MARTINA) NAVRATILOVA
(NADIA) COMANECI	OLGA KORBUT
(LINDSAY) DAVENPORT	PEGGY FLEMING
(DOROTHY) HAMILL	PICABO STREET
(MARTINA) HINGIS	(MARIA) SHARAPOVA
JANET EVANS	SONJA HENIE
(SHAWN) JOHNSON	(ANNIKA) SORENSTAM
(NANCY) KERRIGAN	STEFFI GRAF
(NASTIA) LIUKIN	(KATHY) WHITWORTH
LORENA OCHOA	(VENUS) WILLIAMS

34 | Fitting Words

In this miniature crossword, the clues are listed randomly and are numbered for convenience only. It is up to you to figure out the placement of the 9 answers. To help you, we've inserted one letter in the grid, and this is the only occurrence of that letter in the completed puzzle.

1. Wheel shaft

2. Born earlier

3. Banished person

4. Snow vehicle

5. His and _____

6. Catty comment?

7. Swampland

8. Unwanted plants

9. Take the bus

	A		

35 | Code-doku

Solve this puzzle just as you would a sudoku. Use deductive logic to complete the grid so that each row, column, and 3 by 3 box contains the letters AEJKLMOPS. When you have completed the puzzle, unscramble those letters to reveal the name of the 11th president of the United States.

L	E	M						J
	K				S			
O		L	P			M		E
	A				E			
P	S		M	K				O
	O		L			K		
	P		A	M			O	L
		E					M	
M		S						K

Answer: _____

36 | Medical Anagram

EASY

Fill in the blanks in the sentence below with two 8-letter words that are anagrams of each other.

The doctor prescribed a _____ to settle down the high-strung man, but warned him that he will likely experience unpleasant side effects if he _____ from the recommended dosage.

37 | Ohio Anagram

EASY

What 3 words, formed by different arrangements of the same 6 letters, can be used to complete the sentence below?

The joyriders _____ around _____, Ohio, and watched as stores were _____ during the riot.

38 | DIY Crossword

Fit the given words into the crossword grid. But
be careful with your selections—more words are
provided than are needed.

ADD	ME	SLED
AVER	OLIO	STRIP
DIVE	OMEN	TI
DOT	QUACK	VOTER
EAR	ROE	

39 | Ahoy Matey!
by Alpha Sleuth™

Move each of the letters below into the grid on the next page to form common words. You will use each letter once. The letters in the numbered cells of the grid correspond to the letters in the phrase below the grid. Completing the grid will help you complete the phrase and vice versa. When finished, the grid and phrase should be filled with valid words, and you will have used all the letters in the letter set.

Hint: The numbered cells in the grid are arranged alphabetically, so the letter in the cell marked 1 will appear in the alphabet before the letter in the cell marked 2, and so on.

A	B	C	D	E	F	G	H	I	J	K	L	M
N	O	P	Q	R	S	T	U	V	W	X	Y	Z

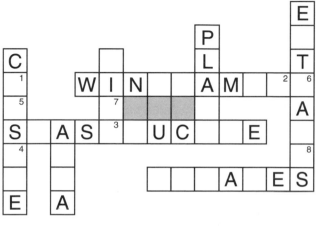

40| Name Calling

Decipher the encoded words in the quote below using the numbers and letters on the phone pad. Remember that each number can stand for 3 or 4 possible letters.

"A hot dog at the 2–2–5–5–4–2–6–3 beats 7–6–2–7–8 2–3–3–3 at the Ritz."

—Humphrey Bogart

41 | Elevator Words

Like an elevator, words move up and down the "floors" of this puzzle. Starting with the first answer, the second part of each answer carries down to become the first part of the following answer. With the clues given, complete the puzzle.

1. Loose _____

2. _____

3. _____ _____

4. _____ _____

5. _____ _____

6. _____

7. _____ Frost

1. Uncontrollable one

2. Solid missile made for firing

3. Sox or Cubs

4. Seltzer cousin

5. Saltine

6. Person of marked excellence

7. Personification of winter weather

42 | Grid Fill

To complete this puzzle, place the given letters and words into the shapes in this grid. Words and letters will run across, down, and wrap around each shape. When the grid is filled, each row will contain one of the following words: candy, caramel, cocoa, cream, minty, sugar, vanilla.

1. C, O, U, Y

2. EA, LA, MA, SC, VA

3. AND, CAM, NIL

4. CROC, GARY, MELT, RAIN

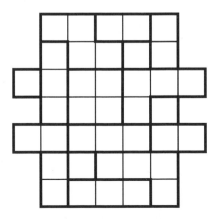

43 | Cast-a-Word

There are 4 dice, and there are different letters of the alphabet on the 6 faces of each of them (each letter appears only once). Random throws of the dice produced the words in this list. Can you figure out which letters appear on each of the 4 dice?

BLOT	MOAT
CAKE	MUCH
CITY	PEWS
CRAM	RASP
DICE	SALT
FLAG	VIBE
HALF	WINE
JARS	ZAPS

44 | Codeword

The letters of the alphabet are hidden in code: Each is represented by a random number from 1 through 26. With the letters already given below, complete the crossword puzzle on the next page with English words and break the code.

1	2	3	4	5	6	7	8	9	10	11	12	13
					A							

14	15	16	17	18	19	20	21	22	23	24	25	26
	P							O			L	

	4		22		10		6		2		4	
7	22	19	24	11	13		10	25	8	17	13	11
	19		6		6		8		10		22	
22	15	6	25		26	19	2	15	6	4	9	10
	25				15		1		24		1	
15	1	24	8	2	22	11		10	26	6	24	11
			26		22		18		1			
20	19	8	15	10		12	1	2	2	8	3	17
	3		24		23		12				8	
26	1	26	22	24	8	5	1		24	1	1	2
	23		23		21		25		22		4	
10	1	23	1	24	1		24	19	16	8	1	10
	3		2		3		14		1		10	

ABCDEFGHIJKLMNOPQRSTUVWXYZ

45 | Who Is . . . ?

Cryptograms are messages in substitution code.
Break the code to read a fact about Alex Trebek.
For example, THE SMART CAT might become FVO
QWGDF JGF if **F** is substituted for **T**, **V** for **H**, **O** for
E, and so on.

KD 1997, ZF ZYGLFJ "HZFFN YP

PYILWDF" HZKNF CUL GURUX LYYX YTFI

"RFYCUIJB!" LZF GHKLQZFIYY HUG UD

UCIKN PYYNG' JUB RYXF.

_____

_____

_____

_____

A rebus follows its own type of alphabet: a mixture of letters, symbols, and pictures. Look carefully at the rebus below. You should be able to "read" the answer to the clue in the puzzle's title.

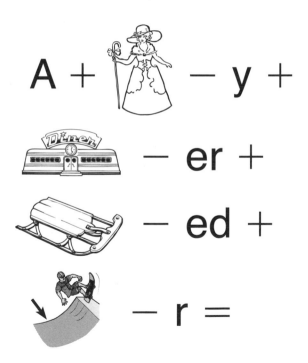

47 | 4-Letter Anagrams

Fill in the blanks in each sentence below with
4-letter words that are anagrams (rearrangements of
the same letters) of one another.

1. The magician always waves his _____ at
   the crack of _____.

2. Junior played a _____ in setting the
   mouse_____.

3. This blindfold doesn't _____ you from
   sneaking a _____.

4. These barbecue _____ are so big they
   each require more than one _____.

5. A _____ water-skier stays in the
   _____ of the boat.

6. _____-flying _____ go hungry.

7. I've heard the _____ delivery in
   _____, Peru, is unreliable.

8. The brewery's four best _____ are rarely on _____.

9. If your _____ of soup is too hot, it is a good idea to _____ on it.

10. The _____ of dinner cooking came through the kitchen _____.

11. If you want a slice of _____ in your drink, you'll have to walk a _____ to the nearest store.

12. I don't _____ who wins the horse _____.

13. Cain's brother _____ was an _____ shepherd.

14. A great river like the _____ in Egypt rarely flows in a straight _____.

15. The student went to climb the _____ with a few of his _____ from school.

48 | Patriotic Clothes

EASY

ACROSS

1. Many a new driver
9. Dundee dweller
13. Classic Caddy
14. Vagabond
15. Cloaked folklore heroine
17. Former big name in long distance, briefly
18. "Don't go!"
19. Korean auto
20. Inscribed pillar
23. Like fresh cake
25. Quick on the uptake
29. Honor with a party
30. Traditional headwear of good guys
32. Layer of paint
34. Fashion
35. Deodorant brand
37. Dental filling
41. Sch. for ministers
42. Pro _____ (in proportion)
46. Before, in verse
47. Literary women nicknamed for their hosiery
51. Egyptian snakes
52. On the move
53. Big name in oil
54. Connects with

DOWN

1. Contract conditions
2. Vote into office
3. Comedian Murphy
4. Neither companion
5. Former Bush spokesman Fleischer
6. Wanders for pleasure
7. Prepare copy
8. Columnist Barrett
9. "Quiet down!"
10. Snacks sold by Girl Scouts
11. Woodwind player
12. Until now
16. Workout place
21. Christine of "Chicago Hope"
22. Yale student
24. Time and again
26. Many "Star Wars" characters, briefly
27. Part of AARP: abbr.
28. "Love _____ neighbor..."
30. Exercise apparel

31. Will Smith title role
32. "Rock the _____"
33. Threat words
36. J and Dre
38. First Soviet premier
39. Trade talk
40. Binary question
43. "They're _____ again!"

44. Collette of "In Her Shoes"
45. Very top
48. Snaky shape
49. Some boxing Ws
50. "...see _____ will believe..."

49 | Theme Park

This "ride" has a theme, but we can't tell you what it is. Place all the words in the boxes below—when you do, read the word created in the outlined boxes, from top to bottom, to reveal what the theme is.

PAGEBOY

~~FLIP~~

~~FRENCH TWIST~~

~~BRAID~~

AFRO

PONYTAIL

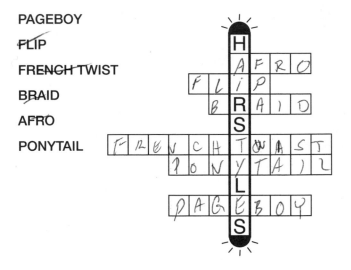

50 | Diamond Cut

Follow the arrows to solve each clue and complete the grid.

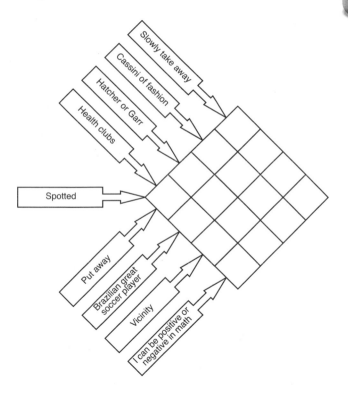

Slowly take away

Cassini of fashion

Hatcher or Garr

Health clubs

Spotted

Put away

Brazilian great soccer player

Vicinity

I can be positive or negative in math

51 | Between the Lines

Below are five 3-word sets, where the middle word
is undefined. All 3 words in each set are arranged
in alphabetical order. Unlocking the defined words
makes it possible to discover the middle word.
When complete, rearrange the middle words in the
spaces at the bottom of the next page to reveal a
quote from Ralph Waldo Emerson.

Example: **putter:** to work at random; tinker
puzzle
pygmy: one of a race of dwarfs

1. ____ ____ ____ o o ____ ____: Joe of gum fame

____ ____

____ ____ a ____ h: where land and water meet

2. ____ ____ ____ ____: fairy tale beginning

____ ____ e

____ n ____ y: merely

3. ___ ___ x: candle material

___ ___ y

___ ___: us

4. ___ a u ___ ___: ghost's verb

___ ___ v ___

___ ___ ___ ___ c: chaos

5. o ___ ___ ___ ___: edible bulb

___ ___ ___ ___

___ ___ ___ ___ ___ ___ ___ ___ o e i a:
crash, bang, boom, e.g.

"The _____ _____ to _____ a

friend is to _____ _____."

52 | Shrouded Summary

Hidden in the word search on the next page is a summary of a well-known novel. The words you need to find are listed below in alphabetical order; in the word search they are presented in an order that makes more sense. The words may be found in a straight line horizontally, vertically, or diagonally. As a bonus, name the novel and its author.

AGELESS	LIFESTYLE
BACHELOR'S	PAINTING
BEHIND	REPOSITORY
DEBAUCHED	TRUTH
DISPLAYING	TURNS
HIDDEN	UGLY
INTO	

Novel and author: _____

```
H D H Z K L S J D R B Q T Q P
E Z S I L I F E S T Y L E C A
O H Y O X N B S Z N F F K N I
R B K V C A R N M H I D D E N
O A I A U P L Q D R Y Z U R T
X C R C H A S V Z E W J P U I
Y H H S M Z E E X P E Z R Z N
O E I C D C N I O O T N I Z G
D L Q F N A C O Q S S A W E D
P O M Z I C F D X I E V K D B
S R M U H T U R T T S G E T F
S S E L E G A G O O C B E M D
K L F Q B W V I L R E Y Z W U
C L S D I S P L A Y I N G V W
P C H K M K U D Q R R R V U D
```

53 | Word Ladder

Use the clues to change just one letter on each line to go from the top word to the bottom word. Do not change the order of the letters. You must have a common English word at each step.

RINGO

_____ victory cry

_____ beatnik's drum

_____ bell sounds

_____ certain investments

_____ diver's fear

_____ used to make necklaces or bracelets

_____ zoo attractions

_____ scorches

_____ they come out at night

STARR

54 | Double Jumble

It's 2 jumbles in one! First, unscramble the 7 letters under each row of squares to form common English words. When you've done this, unscramble the letters running down each column in the blackened boxes to reveal 2 more words.

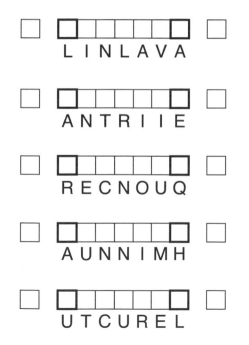

L I N L A V A

A N T R I I E

R E C N O U Q

A U N N I M H

U T C U R E L

55 | Anagram Sentences

What 2 words, formed from different arrangements of the same 5 letters, can be used to complete the sentences below?

1. My _____ necklace looked much _____ against my suntanned skin.

2. During a protest _____ I lost my lucky _____.

3. When I _____ a small party, I can fit all that I need in a single _____.

4. When the telephone _____, the woman _____ because she knows it must be her boyfriend calling.

5. The private _____ of some people are often hidden behind _____ of secrecy.

56 | Rembrandt Was One

A rebus follows its own type of alphabet: a mixture of letters, symbols, and pictures. Look carefully at the rebus below. You should be able to "read" the answer to the clue in the puzzle's title.

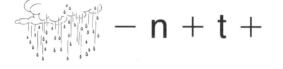 +

 − n + t +

 − l +  − a +

 − be =

57 | Tangled Words

Think of this puzzle like a word search, only in reverse. Rather than finding the words in the grid, your job is to fill them in. Words begin only from the letters given in the shaded boxes, and they appear in a straight line horizontally, vertically, or diagonally. When complete, every word will have been used, and the grid will have no empty squares. Two words have been placed to get you started.

ALTO	EXHAUST	PRACTICE
ASSERT	FLIP	RAPID
~~AUDIO~~	FLYPAPER	ROVES
AWAKE	FOOTPRINT	SINKS
COOKER	HEARTEN	SKATER
COVENANT	PAGEANT	SQUARE
CREVICE	PANG	SQUINT
CUCKOO	PARTY	STAKES
EAGERLY	PEEK	STARBOARD
ENTICED	PIERCE	STEWS
EXCEPT	POETRY	STRENGTH

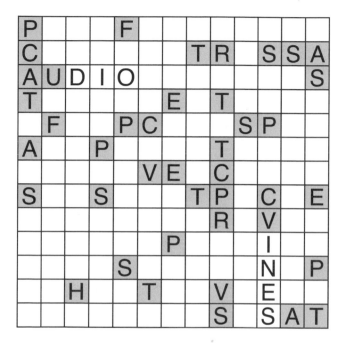

STUDIES	TRANSIT	VIEWS
SUPPER	TRAPPED	~~VINES~~
TASKS	TREATMENT	VOCAL
TETHER	TREND	
TICKET	UNFOLD	

58 | Codeword

The letters of the alphabet are hidden in code: Each is represented by a random number from 1 through 26. With the letters already given below, complete the crossword puzzle on the next page with English words and break the code.

1	2	3	4	5	6	7	8	9	10	11	12	13

14	15	16	17	18	19	20	21	22	23	24	25	26
	S		O		K							

Codeword puzzle grid (13×13). Numbered cells (blanks filled with numbers 1–26); shaded cells shown as ■.

15	10	17	11	11	18	■	■	12	■	6	2	12
■	17	■	17	■	16	5	4	24	23	■	2	
12	17	5	17	3	3	17	■	12	■	5	■	15
■	15	■	19	■	4	■	4	10	21	17	15	
11	23	5	12	23	4	21	23	■	2	■	2	
■	13	■	21	■	15	■	17	■	16	10		
2	15	15	7	23	15	■	23	13	3	17	22	23
13	■	21	■	22	■	26	■	21	■	23	■	
1	■	5	■	8	17	21	26	23	5	23	22	
23	14	2	21	15	■	21	■	23	■	11	■	
5	■	6	■	21	■	23	13	9	17	18	23	22
13	■	23	25	7	4	10	■	17	■	13	■	
17	20	13	■	8	■	17	8	21	7	15	23	

ABCDEFGHIJKLMNOPQRSTUVWXYZ

59 | DIY Crossword

Fit the given words into the crossword grid. But be careful with your selections—more words are provided than are needed.

DOT	ISSUE	ROAST
EYED	OH	SALAD
FA	POT	SO
FEET	RAT	TRUTH
IDEA	RAW	WERE
IF	RIDE	WEST

60 | Add-a-Word

Add one word to each of the 3-word sets to create new words or phrases. For example: In a set including "smith," "fore," and "game," the added word would be "word" (creating "wordsmith," "foreword," and "word game").

1. honey, blue, struck: _____

2. shine, down, chip: _____

3. board, guest, burst: _____

4. mother, rare, science: _____

5. lamp, liquid, vapor: _____

6. bar, parking, time: _____

61 | That's Easy!

ACROSS

1. "_____ at 'em!"
6. Consume
9. Number cruncher: abbr.
12. Kind of skeleton
13. Aye's opposite
14. It's measured in degrees
15. "That's easy!"
17. Letter after sigma
18. "Zuckerman Unbound" novelist
19. Ump's call
20. Sink's alternative
21. Cunning
22. Write quickly
23. Flat replacement
24. Shakespeare, for one
25. Poker phrase
26. "That's easy!"
29. Wax-resistant cloth dyeing technique
30. Feature of a wicked witch
31. Some tournaments
32. Supporter of arms: abbr.
33. Technology behind many film effects: abbr.

36. "The Last Time I Saw You" author Elizabeth
37. "Eat Here and Get _____"
38. Corner pieces
39. Support system?
40. "That's easy!"
42. Tennis call
43. _____ Harbour, Florida
44. Staring intently
45. Before, in poetry
46. Did lunch
47. Special Forces cap

DOWN

1. Hideouts
2. Rave about
3. Like the air around Niagara Falls
4. Classic war film with Hawkeye and Hot Lips
5. _____ Lilly and Company
6. Like a real page-turner, slangily
7. 2010 Angelina Jolie action movie
8. Hurricane's center
9. Stagehand's access

10. "A _____ Home Companion"
11. Insight
16. Actor Dudley
20. Water balloon sound
22. Child's game played on the floor with a ball
23. Pelvic bones
24. Life form
26. Wall decorator
27. Go over (and over)

28. Language of Iran
29. _____head (doll)
33. Unclouded
34. Pottery finish
35. Speck in the ocean
37. Source of milk for chèvre
38. U2 guitarist The _____
40. Hoops group: abbr.
41. Blah-blah-blah

62 | Code-doku

Solve this puzzle just as you would a sudoku. Use deductive logic to complete the grid so that each row, column, and 3 by 3 box contains the letters from the word PUBLISHER.

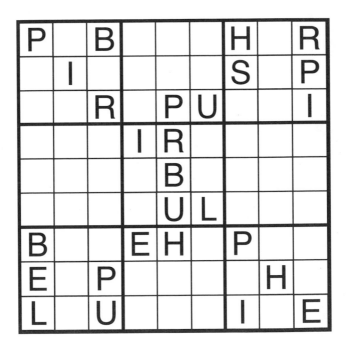

63 | Cast-a-Word

There are 4 dice, and there are different letters of the alphabet on the 6 faces of each of them (each letter appears only once). Random throws of the dice produced the words in this list. Can you figure out which letters appear on each of the 4 dice?

BOWL	HUNK
BYRE	JEST
CELT	LUMP
DRUM	PAWN
FISH	PRAY
GAZE	SITE
GLAD	VISA
HAUL	

64 | Halle Cat

Every word listed is contained within the group of letters on the next page. Words can be found in a straight line horizontally, vertically, or diagonally. They may read either forward or backward. Leftover letters spell an interesting bit of trivia about the actress Halle Berry.

AMEN	LIVING DOLLS
BAPS	LOSING ISAIAH
BOOMERANG	MONSTER'S BALL
BULWORTH	THE PROGRAM
CATWOMAN	QUEEN
DIE ANOTHER DAY	RACE THE SUN
DOROTHY DANDRIDGE	ROBOTS
FATHER HOOD	SOLOMON & SHEBA
THE FLINTSTONES	STRICTLY BUSINESS
GOTHIKA	X-MEN
KNOTS LANDING	

```
I N H I G S L L O D G N I V I L
H A B E H S & N O M O L O S S C
S S E N I S U B Y L T C I R T S
X H O O D O O H R E H T A F L H
G M H A I A S I G N I S O L A L
N B E L E B E R R Y K W A S E D
I M O N S T E R S B A L L I T O
D O R O T H Y D A N D R I D G E
N R O F M T N U S E H T E C A R
A H E D I E A N O T H E R D A Y
L B U L W O R T H S O C A H N O
S C A T W O M A N O L B P M E A
T P T H E F L I N T S T O N E S
O E R P R O M Q U G P E E R U N
N N T H E P R O G R A M A N Q D
K C L A S S P R E S B I D E N T
```

Leftover letters: _____

_____

65 | Chain Grid Fill

To complete this puzzle, place the given words
into the darkened chains in this grid. Words will run
across, down, and diagonally along each chain. It is
up to you to figure out which letters go in the white
squares in the grid. When the grid is complete, each
column of the grid will contain one of the following
words: approach, cinnamon, cloves, cookie,
cupcakes, manage, puppet, skillets, slider, trolling,
vision. We filled in one word to get you started.

1. COP

2. ANNA, CAST, DILL, GONE, LICK, LION,
   LOVE, RING, ROCK, SEEK, TEAM

3. CUMIN

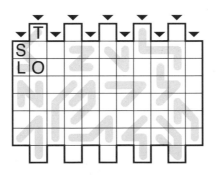

66 | Rhyme Time

Each clue leads to a 2-word answer that rhymes, such as BIG PIG or STABLE TABLE. The numbers in parentheses after the clue give the number of letters in each word. For example, "cookware taken from the oven (3, 3)" would be "hot pot."

1. Cheese store's giveaway (4, 4):

   _____ _____

2. Part of a shoe store's inventory (4, 5):

   _____ _____

3. Ankle-length South Pacific skirt (4, 6):

   _____ _____

4. Reddish-faced pal (5, 5): _____ _____

5. It put the buyer over her limit (5, 6):

   _____ _____

6. Bag-carrier father (6, 5): _____ _____

7. Tan compared to red (6, 5): _____ _____

8. Didn't make a purchase (6, 6):

   _____ _____

9. Perkier pooch (7, 7): _____ _____

67 | Frame Games™

Can you "read" the phrase below?

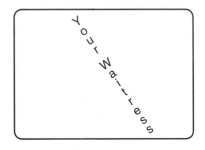

68 | Frame Games™

Can you "read" the phrase below?

69 | Here's to You, Mrs. Robinson

Cryptograms are messages in substitution code. Break the code to read a fact about the movie "The Graduate." For example, THE SMART CAT might become FVO QWGDF JGF if **F** is substituted for **T**, **V** for **H**, **O** for **E**, and so on.

YTPO QFPJADZAQ, BAGXBM BXRLABR,

TQR ITBBXQ GXTMMW IXBX TDD

PAQZFRXBXR LAB MJX KTBM AL

GXQYTNFQ GBTRRAPO MJTM IXQM MA

RVZMFQ JALLNTQ.

_____

_____

_____

_____

_____

70 | Fashionable Anagrams

Fill in the blanks in the sentence below with 8-letter words that are anagrams of each other.

The clothing _____ was _____ to the fact that his work wasn't good enough, so he decided to _____ the entire fall collection.

71 | Can You Remake This Remake?

Rearrange the letters in the phrase below to spell out the title of a movie remake.

    1. HIT FOR FEATHERBED _____

Stumped? Would it help if we gave you the name of one of the film's stars—slightly rearranged, of course?

    2. VAN TERMITES _____

Fit the words into the grid reading across and down.
Each word is used once.

DENTS

OBESE

ORES

OVEN

PROD

PROTO

ROBE

ROVER

TEST

73 | Expectant Mother by Alpha Sleuth™

Move each of the letters below into the grid on the next page to form common words. You will use each letter once. The letters in the numbered cells of the grid correspond to the letters in the phrase below the grid. Completing the grid will help you complete the phrase and vice versa. When finished, the grid and phrase should be filled with valid words, and you will have used all the letters in the letter set.

Hint: The numbered cells in the grid are arranged alphabetically, so the letter in the cell marked 1 will appear in the alphabet before the letter in the cell marked 2, and so on.

A	B	C	D	E	F	G	H	I	J	K	L	M
N	O	P	Q	R	S	T	U	V	W	X	Y	Z

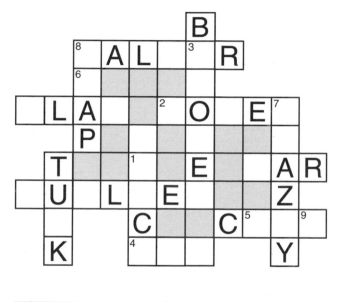

74 | Fitting Words

In this miniature crossword, the clues are listed randomly and are numbered for convenience only. It is up to you to figure out the placement of the 9 answers. To help you, we've inserted one letter in the grid, and this is the only occurrence of that letter in the completed puzzle.

1. Heavenly glow

2. Sound transmission

3. Pinball no-no

4. Figure of Scandinavian folklore

5. Singer _____ Domino

6. Devout

7. Religion

8. Fan favorite

9. Like potato chips or pretzels

75 | Split Decisions

Fill in each set of empty cells with letters that will create English words reading both across and down. Letters may repeat within a single set. We've completed two sets to get you started.

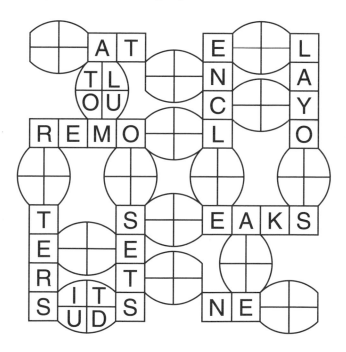

76 | Hail Mary

ACROSS

1. 2009 Nobel Peace Prize winner
6. Switch position
9. Cartoon bark
12. With 55-Across, Mary with an eponymous TV show
13. Evergreen tree
14. That woman
15. River in Paris
16. Pub quaff
17. Put _____ good word
18. "CSI" evidence
20. Fossil finder Mary
22. Painter Mary
26. Makes tea
27. Home plate official
28. Look forward to
30. Tampa body of water
31. R&B singer Mary J.
32. Runner's pace
35. Honking birds
36. Yes to Yvette
37. Spine-tingling
40. Folk musician Mary
43. Mary on a Scottish throne
45. Mexican Mrs.
46. It rises at dawn
47. Chewing material
49. Of yore
53. "Much _____ About Nothing"
54. Can. neighbor
55. See 12-Across
56. Tokyo currency
57. "_____ kingdom come..."
58. Desi of Desilu

DOWN

1. NFL tiebreakers
2. "See ya!"
3. "Thrilla in Manila" boxer
4. Darns
5. Concert venue
6. Three _____ kind (poker hand)
7. Spread through
8. No-cost item
9. "Take _____!"
10. Keep one's subscription going
11. Shows wear, as old clothing
19. "_____ of Two Cities"
21. Museum display
22. Baby bear

23. Docs' org.
24. 007, for one
25. Hip-swiveling dance
29. Golden-_____ (seniors)
31. Potbelly from too many quaffs
32. Coffee, in slang
33. For us
34. American soldiers, for short
35. Model Carangi played by Angelina Jolie

37. Test format
38. Piano exercise
39. Like many overlong sentences
41. Bakery enticement
42. Bravery in battle
44. Rear end
48. Spring month
50. Mafia boss
51. Timeline segment
52. Pince-_____ glasses

77| Word Ladder

Change just one letter on each line to go from
the top word to the bottom word. Do not change
the order of the letters. You must have a common
English word at each step.

HALO

_____

_____

_____

_____

_____

RING

Follow the arrows to solve each clue and complete the grid.

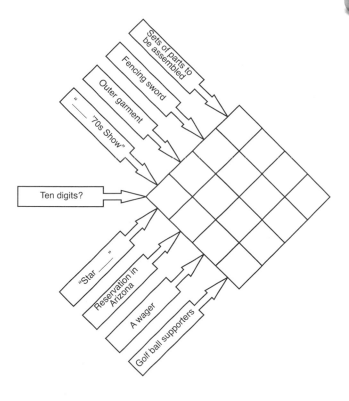

79 | Word Jigsaw

Fit the pieces into the frame to form common words reading across and down. There's no need to rotate the pieces; they'll fit as shown, with each piece used once.

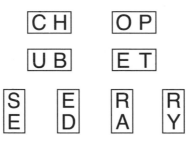

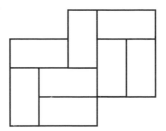

80| Code-doku

Solve this puzzle just as you would a sudoku. Use deductive logic to complete the grid so that each row, column, and 3 by 3 box contains the letters from the word PONYTAILS.

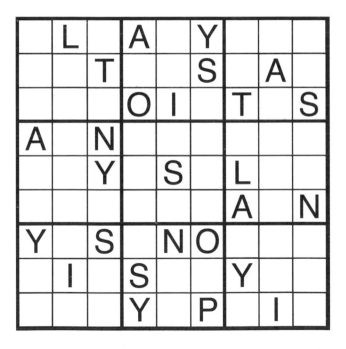

	L		A		Y			
		T			S		A	
			O	I		T		S
A		N						
		Y		S		L		
						A		N
Y		S		N	O			
	I		S				Y	
			Y		P		I	

81 | Arrow Word

This puzzle works exactly like a crossword, only the clues are embedded within the grid. Arrows point to the direction the clue applies, either across or down.

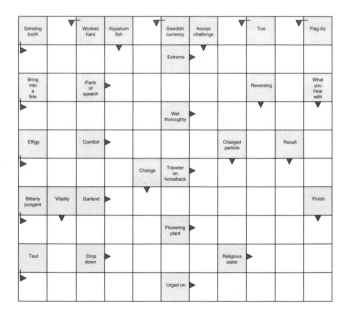

82 | Elevator Words

Like an elevator, words move up and down the "floors" of this puzzle. Starting with the first answer, the second part of each answer carries down to become the first part of the following answer. With the clues given, complete the puzzle.

1. Curtain _____

2. _____ _____

3. _____

4. _____ _____

5. _____ _____

6. _____ _____

7. _____ run

1. Appearance at the end of a show

2. Where a driver may seek assistance

3. Train unit

4. In England, place to keep your wheels

5. Outdoor resting spot

6. Case without a jury

7. Test of a sort

Answer each clue with a 6-letter word. Write the words in either a clockwise or counterclockwise direction around the numerals in the grid. We've placed some letters to get you started.

CLOCKWISE

1. Alerted
2. Plan on
3. Noted speaker
7. Come to terms
8. Stage whispers
9. Masses of people
10. Departs
11. Comes up
13. Remove from text
15. Tastelessly showy
19. Famished
21. Football side
22. Despotic ruler
28. Make longer
30. Mythical giants
32. Systems of beliefs
33. Of the backbone
34. Thin paper
36. Overjoyed
37. In dreamland

COUNTERCLOCKWISE

4. Unmarried
5. Disarm, as a bull
6. Trial by fire
12. Asks for silence
14. Come up with, as a plan
16. Puts together
17. Cliff overhangs
18. Hot-dish stand
20. Wild address
23. Lightweight cord
24. Seeing socially
25. Sinew
26. Granules
27. Creative individual
29. Spinets
31. Divides
35. Metal fasteners

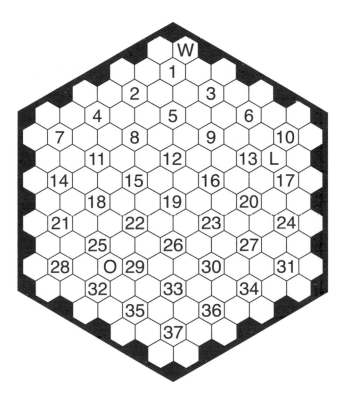

84 | Name Calling

Decipher the encoded word in the quip below using the numbers and letters on the phone pad. Remember that each number can stand for 3 or 4 possible letters.

Oftentimes, my poor mind works just like lightning: One 2–7–4–5–5–4–2–6–8 flash and it's gone!

85 | Chain Grid Fill

To complete this puzzle, place the given words into the darkened chains in this grid. Words will run across, down, and diagonally along each chain. It is up to you to figure out which letters go in the white squares in the grid. When the grid is complete, each column of the grid will contain one of the following words: amazed, armchair, Arnold, bishop, crumbles, detector, distance, equipped, reader, triple, united. We filled in one word to get you started.

1. BOP, NAP, TEA

2. CAST, DEEP, DIME, ITCH, LAIR, READ

3. BRAUN, DETER, POLES, QUART

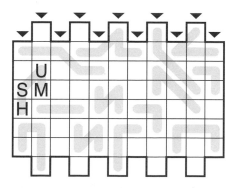

86 | Cast-a-Word

There are 4 dice, and there are different letters of the alphabet on the 6 faces of each of them (each letter appears only once). Random throws of the dice produced the words in this list. Can you figure out which letters appear on each of the 4 dice?

ARTS	ONYX
BALD	PONY
FADE	POUT
GREW	PURL
HULK	STOP
JAMB	WAIT
LUCK	ZINC
LUMP	

87 | Word Pyramid

Fill in the word pyramid by finding the answer to each clue and writing it on the corresponding step. As you move from the top down, each new word is an anagram of the previous word, with one letter added.

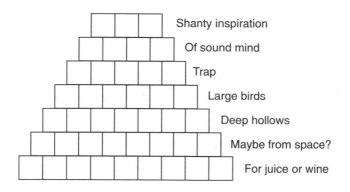

Shanty inspiration

Of sound mind

Trap

Large birds

Deep hollows

Maybe from space?

For juice or wine

88 | Codeword

The letters of the alphabet are hidden in code: Each
is represented by a random number from 1 through
26. With the letters already given below, complete
the crossword puzzle on the next page with English
words and break the code.

1	2	3	4	5	6	7	8	9	10	11	12	13
								D				

14	15	16	17	18	19	20	21	22	23	24	25	26
	Q									W		

10	8	6	18	8	5	4	26	■	14	8	11	12
■	6	■	14	■	3	■	18	■	13	■	17	■
6	20	1	6	23	14	■	14	19	2	5	18	14
■	1	■	2	■	20	21	6	■	5	■	25	■
12	14	4	10	■	6	■	8	17	18	3	14	22
■	6	■	■	■	4	■	■	■	14	■	■	■
14	17	18	14	3	6	■	19	5	9	24	6	22
■	■	■	7	■	■	■	6	■	■	■	1	■
10	14	25	14	18	10	■	7	■	1	6	10	8
■	15	■	11	■	5	11	14	■	17	■	21	■
15	17	21	8	14	9	■	10	14	11	17	18	14
■	6	■	14	■	14	■	8	■	18	■	6	■
16	1	14	9	■	10	21	22	20	14	6	4	10

ABCDEFGHIJKLMNOPQRSTUVWXYZ

89 | Word Jigsaw

Fit the pieces into the frame on the next page to form common words reading across and down. There's no need to rotate the pieces; they'll fit as shown, with each piece used once.

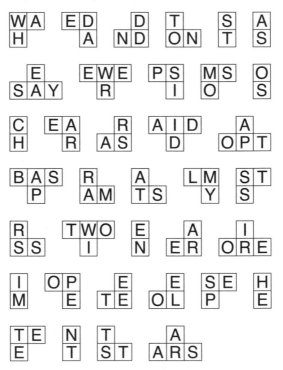

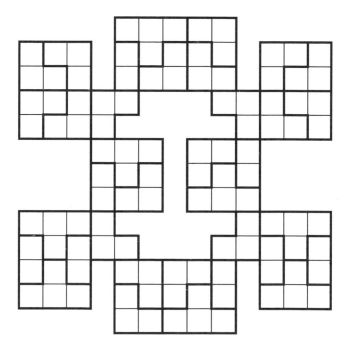

90 | Add-a-Letter

This is a standard word search with a twist: For each word in the list, you must add one letter to form a new word, which you will then search for in the grid on the next page. For example: If the listed word is CARTON, you'd search for CARTOON; if the listed word is OTTER, you might have to search for HOTTER or POTTER. The words can be found in a straight line horizontally, vertically, or diagonally, and may read either forward or backward.

ARROW	INERT
BACK	INSOLENT
BEACH	LUGE
COPPER	MAKER
CURE	MENDER
DANGER	PAINED
DRAGON	PAST
FIGHT	PEACH
GAIN	PEASANT
GALOP	PLANE
GASP	PRIES

```
S T I M U L A T E R E S I G N
G A L L O P X E T T R U C E Z
B L E A C H W F L I G H T L W
T N E V L O S N I F R S J V E
C J K U R N F P N K I P R J A
U B C R P H E A S A N T D B V
R F A I B L Y M E Q J J S P E
S M L L O J A T R P A S T A R
E C B E U R E K T S N S D I E
Z H D E K N A H T A I R A N D
I O H E A R G A T R A W N T N
R P R L Q U C E B G R R G E A
P P P T F I W S O S G I L D E
T E U Y T H R O U G H N E T M
P R E A C H N Q A J S G R K O
```

REIGN   TANKED
RODE   THOUGH
SIFT   TRUE
SIMULATE   WAVER
STILE   WING
TACT

91 | Chaaaaarge It!
by Alpha Sleuth™

Move each of the letters below into the grid on the next page to form common words. You will use each letter once. The letters in the numbered cells of the grid correspond to the letters in the phrase below the grid. Completing the grid will help you complete the phrase and vice versa. When finished, the grid and phrase should be filled with valid words, and you will have used all the letters in the letter set.

Hint: The numbered cells in the grid are arranged alphabetically, so the letter in the cell marked 1 will appear in the alphabet before the letter in the cell marked 2, and so on.

A	B	C	D	E	F	G	H	I	J	K	L	M
N	O	P	Q	R	S	T	U	V	W	X	Y	Z

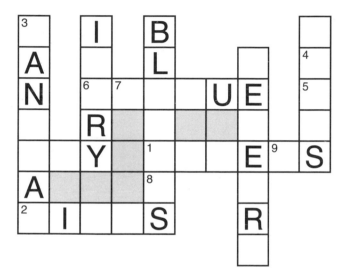

3		I		B						
A				L					4	
N		6	7			U	E		5	
		R								
		Y		1			E	9	S	
A				8						
2	I			S			R			

9	3	6	7	7	4	5	2

9	7	8	1	1

92 | Code-doku

Solve this puzzle just as you would a sudoku. Use deductive logic to complete the grid so that each row, column, and 3 by 3 box contains the letters from the word TRAPEZOID.

		Z			D			O
		T						E
			T	R	Z		D	
T		E		A			O	
	O			D		Z		I
	R		A	I	E			
O						I		
A			R			D		

93 | Romance and Giggles

Cryptograms are messages in substitution code. Break the code to read the quote and its source. For example, THE SMART CAT might become FVO QWGDF JGF if **F** is substituted for **T**, **V** for **H**, **O** for **E**, and so on.

"WZPVZH XWZ KH DWNNRVZWFH,
KLF RF FWIHN QHWB BVMHQN FV KH
NRBBP."
—QVNH GQWZIHZ

_____

_____

_____

94 | Delighted

A rebus follows its own type of alphabet: a mixture of letters, symbols, and pictures. Look carefully at the rebus below. You should be able to "read" the 3-word answer to the clue in the puzzle's title.

95 | Elevator Words

Like an elevator, words move up and down the "floors" of this puzzle. Starting with the first answer, the second part of each answer carries down to become the first part of the following answer. With the clues given, complete the puzzle.

1. Weather _____   1. Form of forecast

2. _____ _____   2. E-mail/news client

3. _____ _____   3. It's faster than first class

4. _____ _____   4. Almost daily delivery spot

5. _____ _____   5. Competitive hobby

6. _____ _____   6. Type of track

7. _____ breaker   7. Tripping device

96 | Tangled Words

Think of this puzzle like a word search, only in reverse. Rather than finding the words in the grid, your job is to fill them in. Words begin only from the letters given in the shaded boxes, and they appear in a straight line horizontally, vertically, or diagonally. When complete, every word will have been used, and the grid will have no empty squares. Two words have been placed to get you started.

BAZAAR	HOTEL	PRONE
DIRTY	HURRAH	PRUNE
DONE	LATHER	PURPLE
DOUBLY	LEASES	PUZZLE
EARRING	LIFT	READAPT
EIDER	PEEKED	REAR-END
EMBERS	PEPPER	REHASH
EULOGY	POOCH	ROSY
HAPHAZARD	PRESTO	ROUGE
HARSHER	PRETEND	RUTHLESS
HOISTED	PRETZELS	SEWN

SIGN	THROES	~~ZEBRA~~
SPELLER	TISSUE	ZENITH
STASHED	USER	ZIPPER
SWAP	YOUNGER	
SWING	~~ZEALOT~~	

DIFFICULT

ACROSS

1. Cuff link's spot
5. Third degree?: abbr.
8. Romanov ruler
12. Pained response
13. Like steak tartare
14. Cronyn of "The Pelican Brief"
15. Scamper
16. Had brunch
17. Beautiful race in "The Time Machine"
18. "Breakfast at Tiffany's" star
21. Wrath
22. "Akeelah and the _____" (2006 film)
23. Debra of "Rachel Getting Married"
26. Kevin of "Beyond the Sea"
30. Per unit
31. It's chained in Alaska
32. Overacts
35. "Key Largo" star Humphrey
37. Hard drinker
38. Perfect test score

39. "Oops! . . . I Did It Again" singer
46. Ballerina's outfit
47. Anatomical duct
48. Vaccination
49. F-16 wing letters
50. Busta Rhymes album
51. Scandinavian capital
52. Feudal slave
53. Bottom-line
54. Josh Groban Christmas album

DOWN

1. Davenport
2. "Little" girl of comics
3. Long Island _____ tea
4. 1983 film about the Mercury Seven
5. "Gloria Patri" is one
6. "Thirty days _____ . . ."
7. Uncool guys
8. Sonny & Cher hit
9. "Star Trek" navigator
10. Cupid
11. Jockey's strap
19. Before, in verse
20. Get-up-and-go
23. Bitsy

1
2
3
4
5
6
7
8
9
10
11
12
13
14
15
16
17
18
19
20
21
22
23
24
25
26
27
28
29
30
31
32
33
34
35
36
37
38
39
40
41
42
43
44
45
46
47
48
49
50
51
52
53
54

24. "_____ . . . Sasha Fierce": Beyoncé album
25. Sgt.
27. Leon Panetta's old agency: abbr.
28. Drop the ball
29. Nevertheless
33. Near eternity
34. Spielberg or Jobs
35. Jacqueline of "Carolina Moon"
36. Caveman of comics
39. Heat measures: abbr.
40. Tricky move
41. _____-TASS news agency
42. Ivy League school
43. "Now I get it!"
44. Part
45. Short-runway plane: abbr.

98 | Between the Lines

Below are five 3-word sets, where the middle word is undefined. All 3 words in each set are arranged in alphabetical order. Unlocking the defined words makes it possible to discover the middle word. When complete, rearrange the middle words in the spaces at the bottom of the next page to reveal a quote from Wendy Liebman.

> Example: **putter:** to work at random; tinker
> **puzzle**
> **pygmy:** one of a race of dwarfs

1. ___ ___ ___ ___ ___: Goodyear vehicle

   ___ ___ ___ n ___

   ___ ___ ___ ___ k: rapid eye movement

2. ___ ___ ___: a deer

   ___ ___ ___

   ___ ___ g m ___: stated beliefs

3. ___ ___ ___ a: facts

  ___ ___ ___ ___ s

  ___ ___ u ___ ___ ___ ___ ___: female
offspring

4. m ___ ___ u f ___ ___ ___ ___ ___ ___:
make

  ___ ___ ___ y

  ___ ___ ___: Chinese chairman

5. ___ ___ ___ ___: microorganism

  ___ ___ t

  ___ ___ y ___ ___ ___: Old Faithful, for one

"I've been on so _____ _____

_____, I should _____ a _____."

99 | Fitting Words

In this miniature crossword, the clues are listed randomly and are numbered for convenience only. It is up to you to figure out the placement of the 9 answers. To help you, we've inserted one letter in the grid, and this is the only occurrence of that letter in the completed puzzle.

1. Bicker

2. Streamlined

3. Hide and _____

4. Fairy tale monster

5. Whizzes past

6. Calliope, e.g.

7. Heats in the microwave

8. Analyze grammatically

9. Language-class exam

100 Rhyme Time

Each clue leads to a 2-word answer that rhymes, such as BIG PIG or STABLE TABLE. The numbers in parentheses after the clue give the number of letters in each word. For example, "cookware taken from the oven (3, 3)" would be "hot pot."

1. The top she wouldn't wear outside (5, 6):

   _____ _____

2. Special on a cotton fabric (7, 4):

   _____ _____

3. Masticate a main course (4, 4):

   _____ _____

4. Female knitting expert (4, 4):

   _____ _____

5. Good time for a wedding (4, 9):

   _____ _____

6. Risqué sweater material (5, 8):

   _____ _____

7. "Almost Like Being in Love," e.g. (9, 4):

   _____ _____

101 | Split Decisions

Fill in each set of empty cells with letters that will create English words reading both across and down. Letters may repeat within a single set. We've completed one set to get you started.

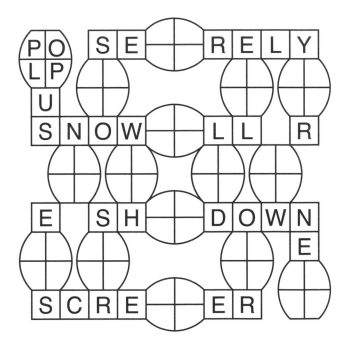

The letters in each of the 12 words below can be rearranged to form the names of 12 countries. Is your geographic knowledge sharp enough to unscramble all 12?

ALSO _____

CHAIN _____

ENEMY _____

LAITY _____

MAIL _____

MOAN _____

PAINS _____

PLANE _____

PURE _____

RAIN _____

REGALIA _____

SERIAL _____

Answer each clue with a 6-letter word. Write the words in either a clockwise or counterclockwise direction around the numerals in the grid. We've placed some letters to get you started.

CLOCKWISE

1. End one's career
3. More ethereal
4. Become more distant
6. Metal fasteners
8. Ran off quickly
11. Professor's security
12. Juicy fruits
13. Southwestern celebration
14. Heaps
17. In a just manner
19. Reason for an action
21. Dissuades
22. Eye shades
25. Turn around
27. Worn away
29. Throws
30. Nappy leathers
31. Medicinal quantity
32. Is buoyant
34. Humiliate

COUNTERCLOCKWISE

2. Concocted
5. Skinnier
7. Decanted
9. Removes lather
10. Isolated fact
15. Slender and graceful
16. Currencies
18. Dispatcher
20. Best clothes
23. Be a sign of
24. In a cheerful manner
26. Paper for wrapping
28. Chin beard
33. Bad treatment
35. Borders
36. Black currant liqueur
37. Pictures

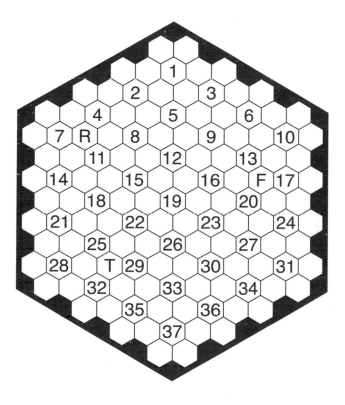

104 | Foreign Dishes

Every word listed is contained within the group of letters on the next page. Words can be found in a straight line horizontally, vertically, or diagonally. They may read either forward or backward.

ARROZ CON POLLO	PIROSHKI
CANNELLONI	RICE PILAF
CHILI CON CARNE	RISOTTO
CHOLENT	SASHIMI
CHOP SUEY	SCALLOPINI
CHOW MEIN	SCAMPI
EGG ROLLS	SHISH KEBAB
FONDUE	SOUVLAKI
FRIED RICE	STROGANOFF
FRITTATA	SUKIYAKI
GOULASH	SUSHI
HAGGIS	TACOS
KIDNEY PIE	TAMALE
KNISH	TEMPURA
LASAGNA	TERIYAKI
MOSTACCIOLI	TOSTADA
OSSO BUCO	TSIMMES

```
C F O N D U E T O S T A D A T
S H I S H K E B A B H S I N K
U T I L S J S C A M P I E G A
S E R L O O Q H I N A L D A T
H R I O I I B V Q R O L V S A
I I C R G C C U H H D B E A T
N Y E G T A O C C H S E U L T
I A P G O R N N A O A O I V I
P K I E Y R O O T G G M R R
O I L Q E O T A F A S X G E F
L K A D O Z T Y F F R O O I S
L H F A F C O Y M U U N M P S
A S N C H O S C U L S I E Y E
C O B V G N I T A I H K F E M
S R M T E P R S E S C A G N M
N I E M W O H C A M K L L D I
G P Y K H L M S C B P V N I S
H I N O L L E N N A C U R K T
Y E U S P O H C N A X O R N V
Q K O G I K A Y I K U S E A P
```

105 | Word Ladder

Change just one letter on each line to go from
the top word to the bottom word. Do not change
the order of the letters. You must have a common
English word at each step.

SLID

———————

———————

———————

———————

———————

HOME

This puzzle works exactly like a crossword, only the clues are embedded within the grid. Arrows point to the direction the clue applies, either across or down.

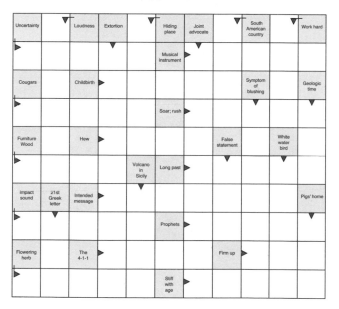

Follow the arrows to solve each clue and complete the grid.

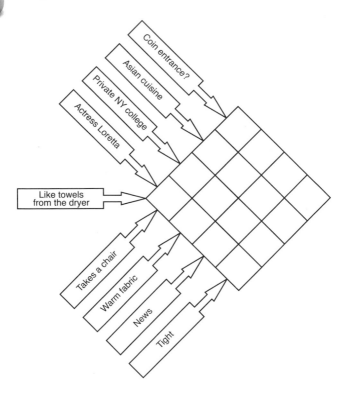

Coin entrance?

Asian cuisine

Private NY college

Actress Loretta

Like towels from the dryer

Takes a chair

Warm fabric

News

Tight

108|Add-a-Word

Add one word to each of the 3-word sets to create new words or phrases. For example: In a set including "smith," "fore," and "game," the added word would be "word" (creating "wordsmith," "foreword," and "word game").

1. loose, fall, big: _____

2. brick, back, arm: _____

3. crystal, room, fast: _____

4. field, post, line: _____

5. boarding, port, word: _____

6. low, rub, town: _____

109 | A Gourmet Guide to Toad Egos

Fill in the blanks in each sentence of the story below with words that are anagrams (rearrangements) of the capitalized words. You'll be able to make a meal of these TOAD EGOS (good eats)!

Thomas Trencherman, master chef, addressed his class. "Snap to, my foodies, time for breakfast! For a snack with coffee, let's have some delicious PARTISAN DISHES _____. Now we'll go through an entire dinner menu, from ZIPPER TEA _____ to RED SETS _____. Let's start with a bowl of the OUR UPS JUDO _____, which today is COLD-WAR CHEM _____, then offer a chilled MICROCHIP STALK _____. Entrée choices will include FUN FUR DARTS _____, consisting of medium-rare WINTRY POKERS _____, served with a steaming hot STARLET BOIL _____. For dessert, a choice of MAUI STIR _____ or the ever-popular EEL CEREBRUM _____. TIBETAN POP _____ to you!"

110 | Code-doku

Solve this puzzle just as you would a sudoku. Use deductive logic to complete the grid so that each row, column, and 3 by 3 box contains the letters from the word MAVERICKS.

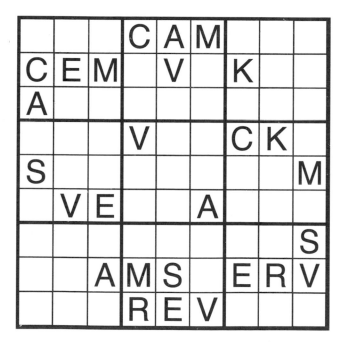

111 | All Creatures Great and Small

A rebus follows its own type of alphabet: a mixture of letters, symbols, and pictures. Look carefully at the rebus below. You should be able to "read" the answer to the clue in the puzzle's title.

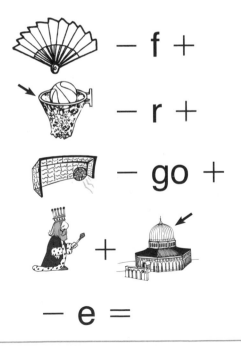

To complete this puzzle, place the given letters and words into the shapes in this grid. Words and letters will run across, down, and wrap around each shape. When the grid is filled, each row will contain one of the following words: barter, births, edible, levers, orange, safety, waffle.

1. F, V

2. BT, ES, FE

3. AIR, GEL, SAW, TEN

4. AFAR, BILE, HERS

5. BORED, TYLER

113 | DIY Crossword

Fit the given words into the crossword grid on the next page. But be careful with your selections—more words are provided than are needed.

AD	FLOATING	MOON
ADDITION	FOB	NA (chem.)
ADO	GAR	NOT
AGREE	GAS	OH
ANAT (abbr.)	GOLDFISH	RH (chem.)
ASH	IAN	SASH
BLOATING	INCH	SINISTER
DRAT	INS	THIGH
EAST	LOB	
EBB	ME	
FA	MINISTER	

114 | Tangled Words

Think of this puzzle like a word search, only in reverse. Rather than finding the words in the grid, your job is to fill them in. Words begin only from the letters given in the shaded boxes, and they appear in a straight line horizontally, vertically, or diagonally. When complete, every word will have been used, and the grid will have no empty squares. Two words have been placed to get you started.

BANJO	JARGON	~~JOCKEY~~
CONJURE	JARRED	JOINTLY
ENJOYS	JASMINE	JOIST
FIJI	JEERER	JOSH
INJECT	JERKS	JOSTLE
INJURY	JERSEY	JOUNCE
JACKPOT	JETS	JOURNEY
JAMB	JEWEL	JOUST
JANUARY	JIFFY	JUBILEE
JAPAN	JIVING	~~JUJUBE~~

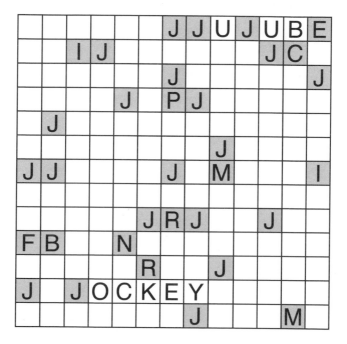

JUMPER	JURY	NINJA
JUNTAS	JUSTICE	PERJURE
JURIST	MAJOR	RAJAH
JURORS	MOJO	REJECT

115 | Codeword

The letters of the alphabet are hidden in code: Each is represented by a random number from 1 through 26. With the letters already given below, complete the crossword puzzle on the next page with English words and break the code.

1	2	3	4	5	6	7	8	9	10	11	12	13

14	15	16	17	18	19	20	21	22	23	24	25	26
	J		E									

20	10	7	11	10	■	9	17	19	18	2	9	17
10	■	10	■	18	■	1	■	■	10	■	2	■
4	■	26	■	25	■	17	■	9	19	24	9	11
16	6	2	12	3	9	7	14	■	19	■	10	■
1	■	17	■	24	■	23	■	9	24	1	6	11
10	11	11	24	19	9	17	8	■	1	■	■	1
9	■	9	■	10	■	■	■	24	■	23	■	17
17	■	■	15	■	10	8	24	25	9	2	23	17
19	17	20	22	11	■	17	■	9	■	11	■	9
■	5	■	6	■	10	11	25	2	19	10	9	17
10	22	13	2	6	■	25	■	4	■	23	■	6
■	2	■	24	■	■	24	■	10	■	2	■	17
22	25	21	19	24	6	9	■	7	24	11	17	19

ABCDEFGHIJKLMNOPQRSTUVWXYZ

116 | Chain Grid Fill

To complete this puzzle, place the given words into the darkened chains in this grid. Words will run across, down, and diagonally along each chain. It is up to you to figure out which letters go in the white squares in the grid. When the grid is complete, each column of the grid will contain one of the following words: bathroom, cartoons, dinosaur, glorious, helium, hot dog, indoor, invent, noodle, Simpsons, vortex. We filled in one word to get you started.

1. BIN, NOD, OIL, ONE, SIN, SOD

2. DIRT, MUGS, OATH, TORN

3. RURAL, STONE, TONER

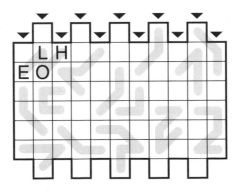

117 | Word Ladder

Use the clues to change just one letter on each line to go from the top word to the bottom word. Do not change the order of the letters. You must have a common English word at each step.

DEVISE

_____ to edit again

_____ to resuscitate

_____ to experience a memory
as if for a second time

_____ to put new borders on

_____ to reduce to a pure state

DEFINE

118 | Cooking

Every word listed is contained within the group of letters on the next page. Words can be found in a straight line horizontally, vertically, or diagonally. They may read either forward or backward.

ASSEMBLE	DREDGE	PICKLE
BAKE	FILLET	POACH
BARBECUE	FLAKE	PREHEAT
BASTE	FREEZE-DRY	PRESERVE
BOIL DOWN	GLAZE	PUREE
BROWN	GRATE	QUICK-FREEZE
CHARBROIL	GREASE	REDUCE
CHOP	GRIND	SAUTÉ
COMBINE	KNEAD	SCRAPE
CONCENTRATE	MARINATE	SIMMER
CRYSTALLIZE	MASH	STEAM
CUBE	MINCE	WHISK
DICE	PAN-BROIL	
DRAIN	PEEL	

119 | Arrow Word

This puzzle works exactly like a crossword, only the clues are embedded within the grid. Arrows point to the direction the clue applies, either across or down.

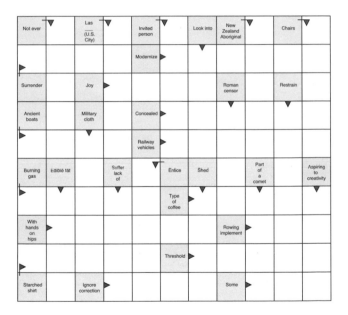

120 | Grape Expectations

Cryptograms are messages in substitution code.
Break the code to read the quote and its source.
For example, THE SMART CAT might become FVO
QWGDF JGF if **F** is substituted for **T**, **V** for **H**, **O** for
E, and so on.

"DFOVUVGGVO UJHFW, AJS LVOF

PYIFW DFZDGF XYDDT."

—YGFCYOQFH MGFPVOK

_____

_____

_____

121 | Honeycomb

Answer each clue with a 6-letter word. Write the words in either a clockwise or counterclockwise direction around the numerals in the grid. We've placed some letters to get you started.

CLOCKWISE

1. Egyptian landmark
4. Heart of bone
6. Temporary residences
8. Like clear night skies
9. Skin art
14. Alibi
15. Most previous
16. Damages beyond repair
17. Army units
18. Grand Turk
19. Highland girls
21. Sister's daughters
22. Wet impacts
23. Wage
25. Concluding part
30. Drawing-off tube
32. Overcome
35. River ends, often

COUNTERCLOCKWISE

2. Voice box
3. Batsman
5. Sleek and gleaming
7. Bovine disease
10. Walk through mud
11. Of the eye
12. Personal preferences
13. Fires a gun
20. Looked and looked
24. Proficient ones
26. Fluttery poplars
27. Chartaceous
28. Stood up to
29. Child's magic word
31. Talking bird
33. Worker bees
34. Visual aids
36. Coastlines
37. Shepherd or sheepdog

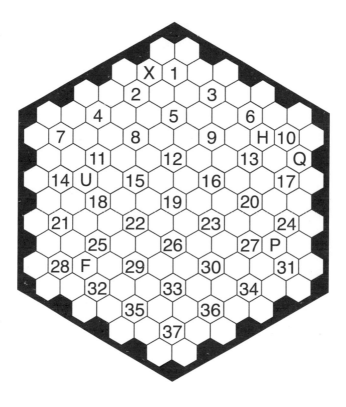

122 | Word Jigsaw

Fit the pieces into the frame on the next page to form common words reading across and down. There's no need to rotate the pieces; they'll fit as shown, with each piece used once.

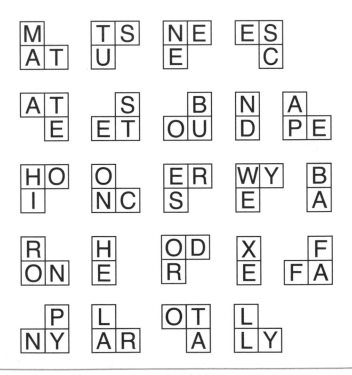

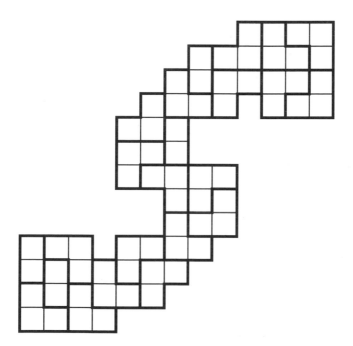

123 | Elevator Words

Like an elevator, words move up and down the "floors" of this puzzle. Starting with the first answer, the second part of each answer carries down to become the first part of the following answer. With the clues given, complete the puzzle.

1. Better _____

2. _____-_____

3. _____ _____

4. _____ _____

5. _____ _____

6. _____ _____

7. _____ off

1. One spouse or the other, perhaps

2. Like a poorly developed plan

3. 49th state dessert

4. You get it by the leg

5. Jelly ingredient

6. Curry favor with

7. Finish

124| Fitting Words

In this miniature crossword, the clues are listed randomly and are numbered for convenience only. It is up to you to figure out the placement of the 9 answers. To help you, we've inserted one letter in the grid, and this is the only occurrence of that letter in the completed puzzle.

1. Raspberry, e.g.

2. Declare openly

3. Guitar's cousin

4. Not flabby

5. 2:1, for example

6. Square number

7. Like Princeton's walls

8. Animal attack

9. Water jugs

125 | Between the Lines

Below are five 3-word sets, where the middle word is undefined. All 3 words in each set are arranged in alphabetical order. Unlocking the defined words makes it possible to discover the middle word. When complete, rearrange the middle words in the spaces at the bottom of the next page to reveal a quote from Joseph Joubert.

Example: **putter:** to work at random; tinker
puzzle
pygmy: one of a race of dwarfs

1. ___ ___ ___ ___ ___ ___ ___: not taking a side

   ___ ___ v ___ ___

   ___ ___ ___: having recently come into existence

2. ___ ___ ___ ___ ___: an area to which a ship may be docked for loading

   ___ ___ ___ ___

   ___ ___ ___ ___ ___: a cereal grain that yields a fine white flour

3. c __ __ __ __ __: a thing that one does habitually

__ __ __

__ __ __ __: attractive, especially in a childish or delicate way

4. __ __ t __ __ __: not arranged neatly and in order

__ n __ __ __

__ __ __ __ __: up to the point in time

5. __ __ __ __ __ __: the grounds and buildings of a university

__ __ __

__ __ __ __ __: an artificial waterway for navigation

" _____ _____ _____ you

_____ _____ ."

ACROSS

1. Half-_____ (espresso order)
4. Tennis units
8. Mascara target
12. MD's organization
13. Roxie _____ in "Chicago"
14. Signs on the dotted line
15. Rocker Ocasek
16. Wine is . . . to Henry Fielding
18. Shaquille of the NBA
20. Delightful sound
21. Wine is . . . to Robert Louis Stevenson
27. Familiar martini go-with
28. Prep bread dough
29. Mouth
31. Fly pattern
33. Aspin or Brown
34. It multiplies by dividing: var.
37. Billiards stroke
40. Wine is . . . to Mark Twain
44. Lah-di-_____
45. Sneezy's sound
46. Wine is . . . to Ernest Hemingway
51. Verb ending?
52. Steve Irwin's favorite reptile, for short
53. Marlin's fish son
54. Zippo
55. "Penny _____"
56. Experience
57. Annapolis grad.

DOWN

1. Chocolate substitute
2. Acid in proteins
3. Bathroom amenity
4. Fence-sitter's question
5. Consume
6. Robert Morse monodrama
7. It's on the cutting edge
8. Rock growth
9. "Wheel of Fortune" buy
10. Jamaican pop music
11. Berlin Airlift president inits.
17. Dinette locale
19. Bermuda's locale: abbr.
22. Mendes of "Hitch"
23. Skin: comb. form
24. Landline device

25. "Norma _____"
26. Jets' gains: abbr.
29. Goat's sound
30. "Mad Men" network
32. Friskies eater
35. _____-ripper
36. "I've Got _____ in Kalamazoo"
38. Wendy sewed it on Peter Pan

39. Vintner's adjective
41. Ponder
42. Stain on lab slides
43. Christmas carols
46. Caesar's quarter grand
47. The elder Gershwin
48. Kat _____ D
49. Buddhist discipline
50. Punk subgenre

127 | Hobby Horse

Which of these is NOT an anagram for a pleasant hobby?

A. Roman Toys

B. Celery Bit

C. Opened Inlet

D. Hotel Syrup

128 | Disney Princesses

Unscramble these phrases to find the names of 5 Disney film heroines.

1. SCAN A PHOTO _____

2. I MET THE DRILL TEAM _____

3. SPECIMENS IN JARS _____

4. DECAL LINER _____

5. TWINE SHOW _____

129 | Split Decisions

Fill in each set of empty cells with letters that will create English words reading both across and down. Letters may repeat within a single set. We've completed one set to get you started.

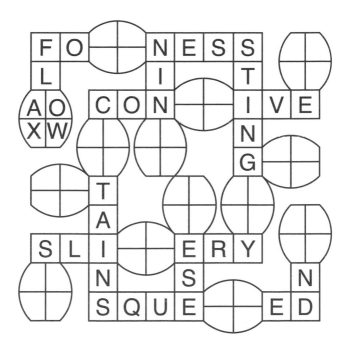

130 | Penalty Box
by Alpha Sleuth™

Move each of the letters below into the grid on the next page to form common hockey words. You will use each letter once. The letters in the numbered cells of the grid correspond to the letters in the phrase below the grid. Completing the grid will help you complete the phrase and vice versa. When finished, the grid and phrase should be filled with valid words, and you will have used all the letters in the letter set.

Hint: The numbered cells in the grid are arranged alphabetically, so the letter in the cell marked 1 will appear in the alphabet before the letter in the cell marked 2, and so on.

A	B	C	D	E	F	G	H	I	J	K	L	M
N	O	P	Q	R	S	T	U	V	W	X	Y	Z

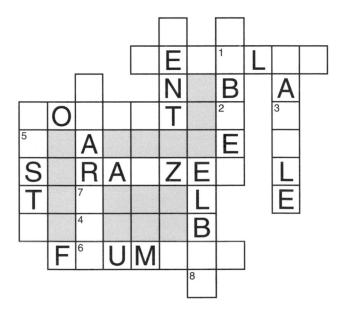

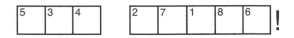

131 | Cast-a-Word

There are 4 dice, and there are different letters of the alphabet on the 6 faces of each of them (each letter appears only once). Random throws of the dice produced the words in this list. Can you figure out which letters appear on each of the 4 dice?

BAKE	HUMP
CAGE	JINX
COAT	NAPE
DARK	OILY
DAWN	SUIT
FIGS	TAXI
HOUR	VERY

132 | Diamond Cut

Follow the arrows to solve each clue and complete the grid.

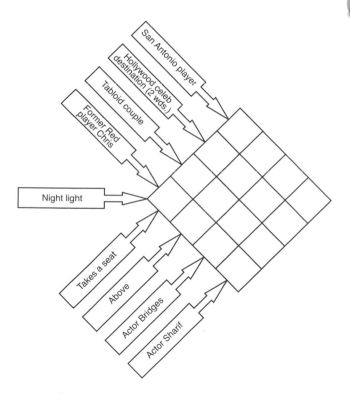

San Antonio player

Hollywood celeb destination (2 wds.)

Tabloid couple

Former Red player Chris

Night light

Takes a seat

Above

Actor Bridges

Actor Sharif

133 | Chain Grid Fill

To complete this puzzle, place the given words into the darkened chains in this grid. Words will run across, down, and diagonally along each chain. It is up to you to figure out which letters go in the white squares in the grid. When the grid is complete, each column of the grid will contain one of the following words: business, doctor, elephant, garden, lumber, minced, mining, palace, promised, relocate, sandwich. We filled in one word to get you started.

1. BUM, GAS, MEN, PAR, SIN, TON

2. BEAR, COIN, DEER, DINE, HANG, MOLD, SEED

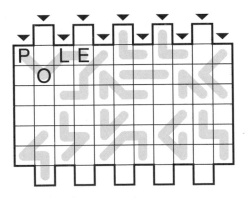

Answers

1 | Wedgewords

2 | Elevator Words

1. LOOK out; 2. outlaw;
3. lawsuit; 4. suitcase;
5. case study; 6. study hall;
7. hallWAY

3 | Word Jigsaw

4 | Theme Park

5 | Food Fun for Fans

TAIL+GATE+PARROT−
(ROT)+TYPE−(PE)=
TAILGATE PARTY

6 | Add-a-Word

1. lily; 2. rose; 3. grace;
4. holly; 5. joy; 6. crystal

7 | What a Jewel

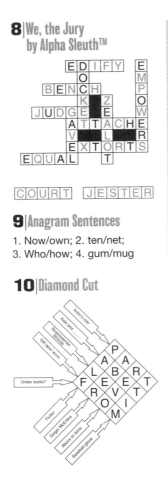

8 | We, the Jury
by Alpha Sleuth™

```
E D I F Y        E
O               M
BENCH       EMP
K   Z         O
JUDGE  ATTACHE R
A T A C H E
V   E   R
EXTORTS
EQUAL   T
```

COURT JESTER

9 | Anagram Sentences

1. Now/own; 2. ten/net;
3. Who/how; 4. gum/mug

10 | Diamond Cut

Actor's role
Aide and __
Businessman Onassis
Gift label word
Under socks?
Flutter
Singer McEntire
Above or dove
Baseball glove

```
        P
      A   A
    L   B   R
  F   E   T
    R   I
    O   M
```

11 | E Pyramid

```
    E
   HE
  SHE
 SHED
SHIED
SHIELD
```

12 | Fitting Words

W	A	G	E	R
A	L	I	V	E
S	O	L	I	D
H	E	L	L	O

13 | Divas

```
M A D O N N A  A R I K A H S  Z
N C C N A  S Y E K A I C I L A  A
S I O  E L O C E I L A T A N  U
W R L G S N D E R W O J D R O B
Q E P K P D M R J M C W I D A B
M N M B N N N X I E F V I R S R
A R A I K A J A L H T D I V B E
R T H O X E N F I I N N C V Y
A N I A E K L E Y W A E E S N I
H C N M G D L S C Y H I R N A L
C I B I R Y S Y W T D T A C R
A T O E O L P P E R I E G S O O
R N H L Y E B L A A U A R N N W
E R Y U A O A J A R G S D A Y
Y A E R S N N R Y Y T K N I P
T J S H O U I C D R E O O A E
Z A Y E C E L A E V A D N B N Y
R O L J G D L N X H S M E E B A
T O N I B R A X T O N  Z B R A
```

14 | Cryptogram

"All hockey players are bilingual. They know English and profanity."

—Gordie Howe

15 | Rhyme Time

1. thug bug; 2. boast most;
3. quick pick; 4. dark bark;
5. drab lab; 6. metal petal;
7. swank bank; 8. damp stamp

16 | The Highly Paid Actress from Down Under

Wives, views

17 | Hobby Horse

B. A is Pottery, B is GORILLA, C is Boating, D is Fishing

18 | Grid Fill

19 | J. Lo

20 | Tangled Words

21 | Wedgewords

22 | Name Calling

As soon as you have graduated from the school of experience, someone adds a new course.

23 | Fitting Words

S	P	A	N	K
C	A	J	U	N
A	G	A	T	E
T	E	R	S	E

24 | Word Ladder

JOKE, coke, cone, cane, sane, SAME

25 | Between the Lines

1. evergreen/every/evidence; 2. rematch/remedy/remember; 3. trot/trouble/trough; 4. pathetic/patience/patient; 5. beside/best/beta

"Patience is the best remedy for every trouble."

26 | Flower Girls

1	P	14	L
2	E	15	G
3	T	16	H
4	U	17	J
5	N	18	D
6	I	19	O
7	A	20	B
8	C	21	F
9	M	22	K
10	S	23	Q
11	V	24	W
12	Y	25	X
13	R	26	Z

27 | Add-a-Word

1. bread; 2. grain; 3. toast; 4. cracker; 5. dough; 6. roll

28 | Split Decisions

Answers may vary.

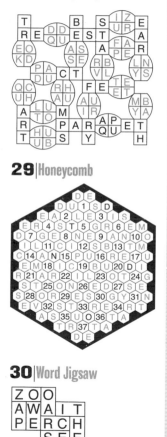

29 | Honeycomb

30 | Word Jigsaw

```
Z O O
A W A I T
P E R C H
    S E E
```

31 | Frame Games™

Stepsisters

32 | Frame Games™

Britney Spears

33 | Sports Legends

34 | Fitting Words

```
M A R S H
E X I L E
O L D E R
W E E D S
```

35 | Code-doku

JAMES POLK

L	P	E	M	K	O	A	S	J
A	K	M	J	E	S	O	L	P
O	S	J	L	P	A	M	K	E
K	L	A	O	S	J	E	P	M
P	E	S	A	M	K	L	J	O
J	M	O	P	L	E	K	A	S
E	J	P	K	A	M	S	O	L
S	O	K	E	J	L	P	M	A
M	A	L	S	O	P	J	E	K

36 | Medical Anagram

sedative, deviates

37 | Ohio Anagram

tooled, Toledo, looted

38 | DIY Crossword

	S	T	R	I	P
O	L	I	O		
	E		E	A	R
A	D	D		V	
		O	M	E	N
V	O	T	E	R	

39 | Ahoy Matey! by Alpha Sleuth™

PIRATE SHIP

40 | Name Calling

"A hot dog at the ballgame beats roast beef at the Ritz."

41 | Elevator Words

1. LOOSE cannon;
2. cannonball; 3. ball club;
4. club soda; 5. soda cracker;
6. crackerjack; 7. Jack FROST

42 | Grid Fill

43 | Cast-a-Word

1. A B D U W Y

2. C F N O S V

3. E G H R T Z

4. I J K L M P

44 | Codeword

1	2	3	4	5	6	7	8	9	10	11	12	13
E	D	N	C	Z	A	F	I	K	S	T	W	H

14	15	16	17	18	19	20	21	22	23	24	25	26
Y	P	B	G	J	U	Q	X	O	V	R	L	M

45 | Who Is … ?

In 1997, he hosted "Wheel of Fortune" while Pat Sajak took over "Jeopardy!" The switcheroo was an April Fools' Day joke.

46 | Dreaming of Genie

A+LADY−(Y)+DINER−(ER)+
SLED−(ED)+RAMP−(R)=
ALADDIN'S LAMP

47 | 4-Letter Anagrams

1. wand/dawn; 2. part/trap;
3. keep/peek; 4. pits/spit;
5. weak/wake; 6. Slow/owls;
7. mail/Lima; 8. ales/sale;
9. bowl/blow; 10. odor/door;
11. lime/mile; 12. care/race;
13. Abel/able; 14. Nile/line;
15. Alps/pals

48 | Patriotic Clothes

49 | Theme Park

```
        H
    A F R O
  F L I P
    B R A I D
    S
F R E N C H T W I S T
    P O N Y T A I L
    L
    E
  P A G E B O Y
    S
```

50 | Diamond Cut

Slowly take away
Creators of fashion
Hatcher or Darl
Health clubs

Spotted

Put away
Brazilian soccer player
Vicinity
I can for battling of
neglect in math

```
    W E
  O E A N
T E L E
S P E R G
  A I
    S
```

51 | Between the Lines

1. Bazooka/be/beach;
2. once/one/only; 3. wax/way/
we; 4. haunt/have/havoc;
5. onion/only/onomatopoeia

"The only way to have a friend
is to be one."

52 | Shrouded Summary

Hidden painting turns
into repository displaying
ugly truth behind ageless
bachelor's debauched
lifestyle. "The Picture of
Dorian Gray" by Oscar Wilde

```
H D H Z K L S J D R B Q T Q P
E Z S I L I F E S T Y L E C A
O H Y O X N B S Z N F F K N I
R B K V C A R N M H I D D E N
O A I A U P L Q D R Y Z U R T
X C R C H A S V Z E W J P U I
Y H H S M Z E E X P E Z R Z N
Q E I C D C N I O O T N I Z G
D L Q F N A C O Q S S A W E D
P O M Z I C F D X I E V K D B
S R M U H T U R T T S G E T F
S S E L E G A G O O C B E M D
K L F Q B W V I L R E Y Z W U
C L S D I S P L A Y I N G V W
P C H K M K U D Q R R R V U D
```

53 | Word Ladder

RINGO, bingo, bongo, bongs,
bonds, bends, beads, bears,
sears, stars, STARR

54 | Double Jumble

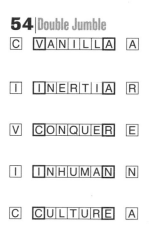

C [VANILLA] A

I [INERTIA] R

V [CONQUER] E

I [INHUMAN] N

C [CULTURE] A

55 | Anagram Sentences

1. pearl/paler; 2. march/charm; 3. cater/crate; 4. rings/grins; 5. lives/veils

56 | Rembrandt Was One

PORT+RAIN−(N)+T+PAIL−(L)+ANT−(A)+BEER−(BE)= PORTRAIT PAINTER

57 | Tangled Words

```
P E E K F L Y P A P E R T
C U C K O O L T R E S S A
A U D I O L R E R A U Q S
T N E M T A E R T A P U T
R F L I P C G N H S P I U
A O N P R O A X T R E N D
N L E C I V E R C I R T I
S D T S N E E T P E C X E
I K R O T N R I R O V E S
T N A E G A P C O Y I K D
S W E T S N K K E G N A P
R E H T E T E E V I E W S
D R A O B R A T S K S A T
```

58 | Codeword

```
S L O P P Y   M   V I M
O   O   G R A Z E   I
M O R O C C O   M   R   S
S   K   A   A L T O S
P E R M E A T E   I   I
N   T   S   O   G   L
I S S U E S   E N C O D E
N   T   D   H   T   E
F   R   B O T H E R E D
E X I T S   T   E   P
R   V   T   E N J O Y E D
N   E Q U A L   O   N
O W N   B   O B T U S E
```

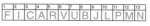

1	2	3	4	5	6	7	8	9	10	11	12	13
F	I	C	A	R	V	U	B	J	L	P	M	N

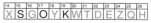

14	15	16	17	18	19	20	21	22	23	24	25	26
X	S	G	O	Y	K	W	T	D	E	Z	Q	H

59 | DIY Crossword

I	F		R	I	D	E
S	A	L	A	D		
S		W	E	S	T	
U		W		A		R
E	Y	E	D			U
		R	O	A	S	T
F	E	E	T		O	H

60 | Add-a-Word

1. moon; 2. sun; 3. star;
4. earth; 5. mercury; 6. space

61 | That's Easy!

L	E	M	M	E		U	S	E		C	P	A
A	X	I	A	L		N	A	Y		A	R	C
I	T	S	S	I	M	P	L	E		T	A	U
R	O	T	H		O	U	T		S	W	I	M
S	L	Y		J	O	T		S	P	A	R	E
			B	A	R	D		A	L	L	I	N
	P	I	E	C	E	O	F	C	A	K	E	
B	A	T	I	K		W	A	R	T			
O	P	E	N	S		N	R	A		C	G	I
B	E	R	G		G	A	S		E	L	L	S
B	R	A		N	O	B	I	G	D	E	A	L
L	E	T		B	A	L		A	G	A	Z	E
E	R	E		A	T	E		B	E	R	E	T

62 | Code-doku

P	U	B	L	I	S	H	E	R
H	I	L	R	E	B	S	U	P
S	E	R	H	P	U	L	B	I
U	L	S	I	R	H	E	P	B
R	P	H	S	B	E	U	I	L
I	B	E	P	U	L	R	S	H
B	S	I	E	H	R	P	L	U
E	R	P	U	L	I	B	H	S
L	H	U	B	S	P	I	R	E

63 | Cast-a-Word

1. A B F K M T

2. C G S U W Y

3. D E H O P V

4. I J L N R Z

64 | Halle Cat

Leftover letters spell: In high school, Halle Berry was editor of the school paper, prom queen, and class president.

```
I N H I G S L L O D G N I V I L
H A B E H S & N O M O L O S S C
S S E N I S U B Y L T C I R T S
X H O O D O O H R E H T A P L H
G M H A I A S I G N I S O L A L
N B E L E B E R R Y K W A S E D
I M O N S T E R S B A L L I T O
D O R O T H Y D A N D R I D G E
N R O F M T N U S E H T E C A R
A H E D I E A N O T H E R D A Y
L B U L W O R T H S O C A H N O
S C A T W O M A N O L B P M E A
T P T H E F L I N T S T O N E S
O E R P R O M Q U G P E E R U N
N N T H E P R O G R A M A N Q D
K C L A S S P R E S B I D E N T
```

65 | Chain Grid Fill

66 | Rhyme Time

1. free Brie; 2. sock stock; 3. long sarong; 4. ruddy buddy; 5. large charge; 6. caddie daddy; 7. duller color; 8. bought naught; 9. merrier terrier

67 | Frame Games™

Tip your waitress

68 | Frame Games™

Holes in her story

69 | Here's to You, Mrs. Robinson

Jack Nicholson, Robert Redford, and Warren Beatty were all considered for the part of Benjamin Braddock that went to Dustin Hoffman.

70 | Fashionable Anagrams

designer/resigned/redesign

71 | Can You Remake This Remake?

1. "Father of the Bride"; 2. Steve Martin

72 | Wedgewords

73 | Expectant Mother
by Alpha Sleuth™

Crossword letters:
```
            B
    W A L K E R
  R         L
F L A P   B O X E S
  P   M   V       N
  T   A   E   J A R
Q U I L T E D     Z
  C   C     C O Z Y
  K   H U G       Y
```

B A B Y   S H O W E R

74 | Fitting Words

F	A	I	T	H
A	U	D	I	O
T	R	O	L	L
S	A	L	T	Y

75 | Split Decisions

Answers may vary.

76 | Hail Mary

```
O B A M A   O F F   A R F
T Y L E R   F I R   H E R
S E I N E   A L E   I N A
      D N A   L E A K E Y
C A S S A T T   B R E W S
U M P     A W A I T
B A Y   B L I G E   J O G
    G E E S E   O U I
E E R I E   T R A V E R S
S T U A R T   S R A
S U N   G U M   O L D E N
A D O   U S A   M O O R E
Y E N   T H Y   A R N A Z
```

77 | Word Ladder

Answers may vary.
HALO, halt, hilt, hint, pint,
ping, RING

78 | Diamond Cut

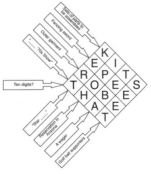

79 | Word Jigsaw

```
      R U B
C H A S E
R O P E D
Y E T
```

80 | Code-doku

S	L	I	A	T	Y	N	O	P
O	N	T	L	P	S	I	A	Y
P	Y	A	O	I	N	T	L	S
A	P	N	T	Y	L	O	S	I
I	O	Y	N	S	A	L	P	T
T	S	L	P	O	I	A	Y	N
Y	A	S	I	N	O	P	T	L
L	I	P	S	A	T	Y	N	O
N	T	O	Y	L	P	S	I	A

81 | Arrow Word

82 | Elevator Words

1. CURTAIN call; 2. call box;
3. boxcar; 4. car park; 5. park
bench; 6. bench trial; 7. trial
RUN

83 | Honeycomb

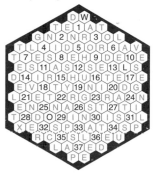

84 | Name Calling

Oftentimes, my poor mind
works just like lightning: One
brilliant flash and it's gone!

85 | Chain Grid Fill

86 | Cast-a-Word

1. A C G H P X

2. B F N S U W

3. D I K M O R

4. E J L T Y Z

87 | Word Pyramid

SEA
SANE
SNARE
RAVENS
RAVINES
INVADERS
VINEYARDS

88 | Codeword

89 | Word Jigsaw

90 | Add-a-Letter

91 | Chaaaaarge It!
by Alpha Sleuth™

92 | Code-doku

R	A	Z	P	E	D	T	I	O
D	P	T	I	O	A	R	Z	E
E	I	O	T	R	Z	A	D	P
T	D	E	Z	A	I	P	O	R
I	Z	R	O	T	P	E	A	D
P	O	A	E	D	R	Z	T	I
Z	R	D	A	I	E	O	P	T
O	E	P	D	Z	T	I	R	A
A	T	I	R	P	O	D	E	Z

93 | Romance and Giggles

"Anyone can be passionate, but it takes real lovers to be silly."

—Rose Franken

94 | Delighted

P+FLEA−(F)+SEA−(A)+D+
GAS−(G)+PUNCH=
PLEASED AS PUNCH

95 | Elevator Words

1. WEATHER outlook;
2. Outlook Express;
3. express mail; 4. mail slot;
5. slot racing; 6. racing circuit;
7. circuit BREAKER

96 | Tangled Words

```
Y L B U O D S P E L L E R
S E S A E L P U O H I E E
O E R K Z E B R A O D F H
R R E P P I Z P E I C T T
E E B R U T H L E S S H A
P A M A Z A I E H T T R L
P R E T Z E L S O E A O R
E E E A L A A L S D S E E
P N R T E H A R R U H S G
S D O N E E O R R S E W N
W I U R Z N Y T R I D I U
A R G T P A D A E R N N O
P Z E N I T H E U L O G Y
```

97 | A Certain Style

```
S L I T   P H D   T S A R
O U C H   R A W   H U M E
F L E E   A T E   E L O I
A U D R E Y H E P B U R N
      I R E   B E E
W I N G E R   S P A C E Y
E A C H           T I R E
E M O T E S   B O G A R T
      S O T   I O O
B R I T N E Y S P E A R S
T U T U   V A S   S H O T
U S A F   E L E   O S L O
S E R F   N E T   N O E L
```

98 | Between the Lines

1. blimp/blind/blink; 2. doe/dog/dogma; 3. data/dates/daughter; 4. manufacture/many/Mao; 5. germ/get/geyser

"I've been on so many blind dates, I should get a dog."

99 | Fitting Words

```
Z O O M S
A R G U E
P A R S E
S L E E K
```

100 | Rhyme Time

1. house blouse; 2. percale sale; 3. chew stew; 4. purl girl; 5. June afternoon; 6. sheer cashmere; 7. "Brigadoon" tune

101 | Split Decisions

Answers may vary.

102 | Geographagrams

LAOS

CHINA

YEMEN

ITALY

MALI

OMAN

SPAIN

NEPAL

PERU

IRAN

ALGERIA

ISRAEL

103 | Honeycomb

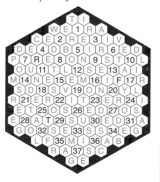

104 | Foreign Dishes

105 | Word Ladder

Answers may vary.
SLID, said, sand, sane, same, some, HOME

106 | Arrow Word

	V		S	Hiding place	Join advocate	P	South American country	S	Work hard
	D	O	U	B	T	C	E	L	L	O
	L		L	A	B	O	R	O		Gaslight time
Coagulate	P	U	M	A	S		S	U	R	G	E
Fountain Wheel	M	C	H	O	P		E	E	O
	T	E	A	K		O	L	D	E	N
	S		M	E	A	N	I	N	G
	S	P	L	A	T		S	E	E	R	S
	H		I	N	F	O		S	E	T
	V	I	O	L	A		R	U	S	T	Y

107|Diamond Cut

108|Add-a-Word

1. foot; 2. yard; 3. ball;
4. goal; 5. pass; 6. down

109|A Gourmet Guide to Toad Egos

Thomas Trencherman, master chef, addressed his class. "Snap to, my foodies, time for breakfast! For a snack with coffee, let's have some delicious DANISH PASTRIES. Now we'll go through an entire dinner menu, from APPETIZER to DESSERT. Let's start with a bowl of the SOUP DU JOUR, which today is CLAM CHOWDER, then offer a chilled SHRIMP COCKTAIL. Entrée choices will include SURF AND TURF, consisting of medium-rare NEW YORK STRIP, served with a steaming hot LOBSTER TAIL. For dessert, a choice of TIRAMISU or the ever-popular CRÈME BRÛLÉE. BON APPÉTIT to you!"

110|Code-doku

111|All Creatures Great and Small

FAN−(F)+RIM−(R)+GOAL−(GO)+KING+DOME−(E)=
ANIMAL KINGDOM

```
S A F E T Y
W A F F L E
B A R T E R
O R A N G E
E D I B L E
B I R T H S
L E V E R S
```

```
  A G R E E   M E
A D O   A   F O B
N   L   S   L O B
A D D I T I O N
T   F A   N A   D
  S I N I S T E R
G A S   N   I   A
A S H   C   N O T
R H   T H I G H
```

```
Y L T N I O J J U J U B E
R E I J N E C N U O J C N
A W N U E A J M T S I O J
U E J R J O P J E T S N O
N J E I U E E A S L A J Y
A R C S R O R U J E T U S
J J T T J G J S M C N R I
I A N N N U U A E A U E N
F M A I B J R J C Y J O J
F B V I N E E A U K G O U
Y I L D E R R A J R P J R
J E J O C K E Y A A Y O Y
E E N I M S A J O S H M T
```

```
B A L S A   T E R M I T E
A   A M   W   A   I
C   Z   P   E   T R O T S
K N I G H T L Y   R   A
W   E   O   V   T O W N S
A S S O R T E D     W   E
T   T   A   O   V   E
E   J   A D O P T I V E
R E B U S   E   T   S   T
  Q   N   A S P I R A T E
A U X I N   P   C   V
I   O   O   A   I   N E
U P F R O N T   L O S E R
```

1	2	3	4	5	6	7	8	9	10	11	12	13
W	I	H	C	Q	N	L	D	T	A	S	G	X

14	15	16	17	18	19	20	21	22	23	24	25	26
Y	J	K	E	M	R	B	F	U	V	O	P	Z

116 | Chain Grid Fill

▼G	▼C	▼D	▼S	▼B

H	L	H	A	N	I	I	I	V	A	I
E	O	O	R	O	N	N	M	O	T	N
L	R	T	T	O	O	D	P	R	H	V
I	I	D	O	D	S	O	S	T	R	E
U	O	O	O	L	A	O	O	E	O	N
M	U	G	N	E	U	R	N	X	O	T
	S		S		S		S		M	

117 | Word Ladder

DEVISE, revise, revive, relive, reline, refine, DEFINE

118 | Cooking

```
P T V W Y F D S G B G R I N D
A O P N Z R X P T R Z L B R A
N B A K E E R N E O A L M Z E
B D I C E E R A T W G T A H N
R F A V H Z S V U N J E E C K
O Z W E W E F L A K E L T O N
I Y A G T D Z I S Y C K S N D
L T H R W R T L L H T C Z C R
E P C C R Y S T A L L I Z E L
Z T U R G L I R Y M E P L N S
E B E R D S B N H A Z T Y T B
N M C E R L S C R A P E R R M
R T V Z O E A W H S K P D A A
F L A I R M E C U D E R R T S
K E L N T E B Z Z T E E I S E
C E T R I K M I N I C S D Z E
I P Z S S R N M N N H E G A M
U Z Y I A M A E I E O R E L B
Q Q H C T B L M D S P V B G L
N W O D L I O B A R B E C U E
```

119 | Arrow Word

120 | Grape Expectations

"Penicillin cures, but wine makes people happy."

—Alexander Fleming

121 | Honeycomb

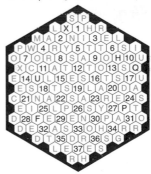

122|Word Jigsaw

123|Elevator Words

1. BETTER half; 2. half-baked;
3. baked Alaska; 4. Alaska
crab; 5. crab apple; 6. apple
polish; 7. polish OFF

124|Fitting Words

B	A	N	J	O
I	V	I	E	D
T	O	N	E	D
E	W	E	R	S

125|Between the Lines

1. neutral/never/new;
2. wharf/what/wheat;
3. custom/cut/cute;
4. untidy/untie/until;
5. campus/can/canal

"Never cut what you can
untie."

126|Wine Is . . .

127|Hobby Horse

B. A is Astronomy, B is
CELEBRITY, C is Needlepoint,
D is Upholstery

128|Disney Princesses

1. Pocahontas; 2. The
Little Mermaid; 3. Princess
Jasmine; 4. Cinderella;
5. Snow White

129 | Split Decisions

Answers may vary.

130 | Penalty Box
by Alpha Sleuth™

ICE   BRAWL!

131 | Cast-a-Word

1. A F J L U V

2. B C I P R W

3. D E M O S X

4. G H K N T Y

132 | Diamond Cut

San Antonio player
Hollywood / Disney destination (2 wds.)
Tisdale couple
Former NBA player Ginóbili

Night light

Takes a seat
Above
Actor Bridges
Actor Sharif

S
P
S T I U
I O R
T O A A
S A T E B O A A
O E M
B O
E

133 | Chain Grid Fill

P R B S E
P R L E D U M A G L M
A O U L O S I N A E I
L M M O C I N D R P N
A I B C T N C W D H I
C S E A O E E I E A N
E E R T R S D C N N G
D E S H T